MW00666911

SPORTY'S®

WHAT YOU SHOULD KNOW™ SERIES

Ground Lesson Guide

for the

Recreational and Private Pilot Training Course Outlines

Sporty's Academy, Inc.
Clermont County/Sporty's Airport
Batavia, OH 45103

Printed in the United States of America
ISBN 0-9715631-8-7

For additional copies, reorder #M726A

Call: 1 (USA) 800.SPORTYS
(776.7897)

Fax: 1 (USA) 800.359.7794
1 (USA) 513.735.9200
sportys.com

11/03

Table of Contents

Preface

The *Ground Lesson Guide for the Recreational and Private Pilot Training Course Outlines* is an aviation knowledge source for the primary flight instructor in outline form. It was developed with the instructor in mind but is also a useful study guide for use by students.

The *Ground Lesson Guide* is a new part of Sporty's *Complete Flight Training Course*™. The *Guide* elaborates on the ground lesson content found in the *Recreational Pilot TCO* (M275A), the *Private Pilot TCO* (M437A), and the *Recreational Pilot to Private Pilot TCO* (M267A). The *Ground Lesson Guide* gives the instructor and the student an expanded explanation for the ground lessons in these TCOs. It is intended to complement the TCOs and Sporty's *Complete Flight Training Course on Interactive DVD*.

The first 15 ground lessons in the *Recreational Pilot TCO* and the *Private Pilot TCO* are the same with only minor exceptions related to the discussion of privileges and limitations. These lessons are covered in this book under the same reference number.

Lesson G16 of the *Private Pilot TCO* corresponds to Lesson G1 of the *Recreational Pilot to Private Pilot TCO*. The relationship between these two courses is shown in the title of the lessons within this book by using dual reference numbers. Use the reference number appropriate to the training track and TCO you are utilizing with your primary students.

Sporty's Academy Staff
Batavia, Ohio
November, 2003

References

Many of the FAA and Sporty's Academy references below were used in the preparation of this manual. Most of the references listed may be purchased from Sporty's by calling 1.800.SPORTYS (776.7897) from the USA or by logging on to sportys.com.

FAA References:

- 14 CFR Part 43 Maintenance, Preventive Maintenance, Rebuilding, and Alteration
- 14 CFR Part 61 Certification: Pilots and Flight Instructors
- 14 CFR Part 91 General Operating and Flight Rules
- 14 CFR Part 97 Standard Instrument Approach Procedures
- 14 CFR Part 141 Pilot Schools
- NTSB Part 830 Notification and Reporting of Aircraft Accidents and Incidents
- FAA-H-8083-1 Aircraft Weight and Balance Handbook
- FAA-H-8083-3 Airplane Flying Handbook
- FAA-H-8083-15 Instrument Flying Handbook
- AC 00-2 Advisory Circular Checklist
- AC 00-6 Aviation Weather
- AC 00-45 Aviation Weather Services
- AC 61-23 / FAA-H-8083-25 Pilot's Handbook of Aeronautical Knowledge
- AC 61-65 Certification: Pilots and Flight Instructors
- AC 61-67 Stall Spin Awareness Training
- AC 61-84 Role of Preflight Preparation
- AC 65-12 Airframe and Powerplant Mechanics Powerplant Handbook
- AC 65-15 Airframe and Powerplant Mechanics Airframe Handbook
- AC 67-2 Medical Handbook for Pilots
- AC 90-48 Pilots' Role in Collision Avoidance
- AC 120-51 Crew Resource Management Training
- AIM Aeronautical Information Manual
- A/FD Airport / Facility Directory
- NOTAMs Notices to Airmen
- AFM/POH - FAA-Approved Flight Manual/Pilot Operating Handbook

Sporty's Academy References:

- M275A Recreational Pilot TCO
- M437A Private Pilot TCO
- M267A Recreational Pilot to Private Pilot TCO
- B2416A Recreational Pilot Flight Training Course on Interactive DVD
- B4165A Private Pilot Flight Training Course on Interactive DVD
- B3247A Recreational Pilot to Private Pilot Transition Flight Training Course on Interactive DVD

LESSON G1 – FAR / AIM, NTSB 830, PTS, & LOGBOOKS

Aeronautical Decision Making and Judgment

- In flying, there are a number of different types of decisions which must be made every time
  - Some are easy, others are more difficult
  - Each must be made using sound judgment as they all may impact the outcome of the flight
- Good judgment can be gained through experience, but this trial-and-error method of learning this important skill can also lead to disaster
  - A pilot must learn early in his flying career how to deal with decision making in general and learn strategies that will lead to effective judgment in a wide variety of situations
- Basically, two types of decisions:
  - Decisions with a time constraint – events requiring immediate action
  - Decisions without a time constraint – allow more time to gather information and consider alternative courses of action
- A large number of accidents could have been prevented if only the pilot had taken more time during preflight to consider the alternatives for these non-time constrained decisions
- Discuss the impact of the pilot's attitude on decision making along with the five hazardous attitudes which the students must learn to recognize in himself:
  - Antiauthority
  - Impulsivity
  - Invulnerability
  - Macho
  - Resignation
- Discuss and have the student develop a Personal Minimums checklist for the next lesson
  - Samples may be found at the end of Chapter 18 in the *Airplane Flying Handbook*
  - You will need to help your student fill in the blanks
- Additional aeronautical decision making (ADM) and judgment information is available in Chapter 18 of the *Airplane Flying Handbook*

14 CFR Part 1

- Before getting started with the regulations, talk to the student about 14 CFR and FAR nomenclature
- 14 CFR Part 1 covers important definitions and abbreviations that may be used in other parts of the regulations
- Ensure that the student understands the key definitions applicable to a Recreational or Private Pilot and where to find them
  - Be sure to include a review of key V speed definitions

14 CFR Part 61 Recreational / Student Limitations

- 14 CFR Part 61 covers the rules for the certification of pilots and flight instructors when not training under a 14 CFR Part 141 approved course of instruction
- Student Pilot Certificate Privileges
  - May fly an aircraft as the sole occupant of the aircraft when properly endorsed and in accordance with limitations set by the flight instructor

- Student Pilot Certificate Limitations (61.89)
  - No passengers
  - No compensation or hire
  - No furtherance of a business
  - No international
  - Minimum of 3 miles visibility (5 night)
  - Must see the surface
  - No required crewmember
  - Any limitations from flight instructor

- Student pilot certificate expires 24 calendar months after being issued (61.19)

- Recreational Pilot Certificate Privileges (61.101)
  - Carry up to one passenger
  - Share expenses (pro rata) for fuel, oil, airport expenditures, or rental
  - Act as PIC on a flight within 50 NM of an airport where trained and endorsed
  - Act as PIC farther than 50 nautical miles with cross-country training and endorsement
    - Must have logbook in possession for these operations

- Recreational Pilot Certificate Limitations (61.101)
  - May not act as PIC if:
    - The aircraft is certificated for more than four occupants, with more than one powerplant, with a powerplant of more than 180 horsepower, or with retractable landing gear
    - The aircraft is classified as a multiengine airplane, powered-lift, glider, airship, or balloon
    - Carrying a passenger or property for compensation or hire
    - For compensation or hire
    - In furtherance of a business
    - Between sunset and sunrise
    - In airspace requiring communication with ATC
    - Flying more than 10,000 feet MSL or 2,000 feet AGL, whichever is higher
    - When the flight or surface visibility is less than 3 statute miles
    - Without visual reference to the surface
    - On a flight outside the U.S.
    - Demonstrating that aircraft in flight to a prospective buyer
    - Being used in a passenger-carrying airlift
    - Towing any object
  - May not act as a pilot flight crewmember on an aircraft requiring more than one pilot with certain training related exceptions
  - A recreational pilot certificate does not meet ICAO requirements
  - Limitations relating to aircraft, airspace, and night flying may be superseded by an instructor's training and endorsement provided that the recreational pilot is the sole aircraft occupant and training for an additional rating
    - Must have logbook in possession for these operations

- Training and an endorsement is required for operating tailwheel airplanes (61.31)

- Recreational Pilot Currency (61.56, 57, & 101)
  - May not act as PIC if pilot has logged fewer than 400 flight hours and has not logged PIC time in an aircraft within 180 days
    - Requires CFI flight training and a logbook endorsement
  - Flight Review in an aircraft for which the pilot is rated – 24 calendar months; or Wings, Checkride, etc.
  - To carry passengers – 3 Takeoffs and 3 Landings as sole manipulator of the controls within previous 90 days (Full stop landings for tailwheel.)
- Notify the FAA within 30 days of a change of address (61.60)
  - If a post box, notify of permanent residence
- Photo I.D. – 14 CFR 61.3, Requirement for certificates, ratings, and authorizations, will now include a photo I.D. in the form of a valid driver's license issued by a U.S. state, the District of Columbia, or a U.S. territory or possession
  - Other suitable forms of identification are a valid federal or state ID card, a U.S. armed forces' ID, credentials that authorize access to airport secure areas, or other identification that the FAA accepts

14 CFR Part 61 Private / Student Limitations

- 14 CFR Part 61 covers the rules for the certification of pilots and flight instructors when not training under a 14 CFR Part 141 approved course of instruction
- Student Pilot Certificate Privileges
  - May fly an aircraft as the sole occupant of the aircraft when properly endorsed and in accordance with limitations set by the flight instructor
- Student Pilot Certificate Limitations (61.89)
  - No passengers
  - No compensation or hire
  - No furtherance of a business
  - No international
  - Minimum of 3 miles visibility (5 night)
  - Must see the surface
  - No required crewmember
  - Any limitations from flight instructor
- Student Pilot Certificate expires 24 calendar months after being issued (61.19)
- Private Pilot Certificate Privileges (61.113)
  - Fly associated with a business as long as it is incidental
  - Candidates of federal elections
  - Share expenses (pro rata) for fuel, oil, airport expenditures, or rental
  - Fly an airlift for a charitable organization
  - Reimbursed for search & rescue
  - Demonstrate an aircraft (200 hours)
  - Tow a glider
- Private Pilot Certificate Limitations (61.113)
  - Can not be paid as a pilot of an aircraft (even as second-in-command)
    - Exceptions listed previously

- Private Pilot Currency (61.56 & 57)
  - Flight Review in an aircraft for which the pilot is rated – 24 calendar months; or Wings, checkride, etc.
  - To carry passengers – 3 Takeoffs and 3 Landings as sole manipulator of the controls within previous 90 days (full stop landings for tailwheel or night where night is considered 1 hour after sunset to 1 hour prior to sunrise)
- Notify the FAA within 30 days of a change of address (61.60)
  - If a post box, notify of permanent residence
- Training and endorsements are required for operating complex or high-performance airplanes, pressurized aircraft capable of operating at high altitudes, and tailwheel airplanes (61.31)
- Photo I.D. – 14 CFR 61.3, Requirement for certificates, ratings, and authorizations, will now include a photo I.D. in the form of a valid driver's license issued by a U.S. state, the District of Columbia, or a U.S. territory or possession
  - Other suitable forms of identification are a valid federal or state ID card, a U.S. armed forces' ID, credentials that authorize access to airport secure areas, or other identification that the FAA accepts

14 CFR Part 67

- A Third Class or better Medical Certificate is required by 61.23
  - Valid for Student and Private Pilot privileges for 36 Calendar Months if under age 40
  - Otherwise it is valid for 24 Calendar Months
- 14 CFR Part 67 explains the requirements for the various classes of medical certificate

14 CFR Part 91

- 14 CFR Part 91 covers the general operating and flight rules to which a pilot must adhere
- During this lesson, be sure and cover sections 3, 9, 13, 15, 17, 19, 103, 105, 107, 111, 113, 119, 126, 127, & 137 and any others deemed appropriate

14 CFR Part 141

- 14 CFR Part 141 covers the rules for certificated pilot schools
- Ensure that the student knows which set of certification rules he is training under

NTSB 830

- An aircraft accident means an occurrence associated with the operation of an aircraft which takes place between the time any person boards the aircraft with the intention of flight and all such persons have disembarked, and in which any person suffers death or serious injury, or in which the aircraft receives substantial damage
- Fatal injury means any injury which results in death within 30 days of the accident
- Serious injury means any injury which:
  - Requires hospitalization for more than 48 hours, (within 7 days of injury)
  - Results in a fractured bone (except simple fractures of fingers, toes, or nose)
  - Causes severe hemorrhages, nerve, muscle, or tendon damage
  - Involves any internal organ
  - Involves second- or third-degree burns, or any burns affecting more than 5 percent of the body's surface

- Substantial damage means damage or failure which adversely affects the structural strength, performance, or flight characteristics of the aircraft, and which would normally require major repair or replacement of the affected component
  - Engine failure or damage limited to an engine if only one engine fails or is damaged, bent fairings or cowling, dented skin, small punctured holes in the skin or fabric, ground damage to rotor or propeller blades, and damage to landing gear, wheels, tires, flaps, engine accessories, brakes, or wingtips are not considered "substantial damage" for the purpose of this regulation
- Immediately notify the NTSB when an aircraft accident or any of the following listed incidents occur:
  - Flight control system malfunction or failure
  - Inability of any required flight crewmember to perform normal flight duties as a result of injury or illness
  - Failure of structural components of a turbine engine (certain exclusions)
  - In-flight fire
  - Aircraft collide in flight
  - Damage to property, other than the aircraft, estimated to exceed $25,000 for repair or fair market value in the event of total loss, whichever is less
  - For large multiengine aircraft there are other conditions requiring a report
- Immediately notify the NTSB when an aircraft is overdue and is believed to have been involved in an accident
- Notification should include the following information, if available:
  - Type, nationality, and registration marks of the aircraft
  - Name of owner, and operator of the aircraft
  - Name of the pilot-in-command
  - Date and time of the accident
  - Last point of departure and point of intended landing of the aircraft
  - Position of the aircraft with reference to some easily defined geographical point
  - Number of persons aboard, number killed, and number seriously injured
  - Nature of the accident, the weather and the extent of damage to the aircraft, so far as is known; and
  - A description of any explosives, radioactive materials, or other dangerous articles carried
- To the extent possible, the wreckage should be protected and left undisturbed, except:
  - To remove injured or trapped persons
  - To protect the wreckage from further damage
  - To protect the public from injury

AIM

- The Aeronautical Information Manual (AIM) is designed to provide the aviation community with basic flight information and ATC procedures for use in the National Airspace System (NAS) of the United States
- This manual contains items of interest to pilots concerning health and medical facts, factors affecting flight safety, a pilot / controller glossary of terms used in the ATC System, and information on safety, accident, and hazard reporting

- The AIM is complemented by other operational publications:
  - Notices to Airmen
  - The Airport / Facility Directory, the Alaska Supplement, and the Pacific Chart Supplement
- Ensure that the student understands the basic contents and usage of the AIM
  - Review the major chapter headings

Pilot Logbooks

- A pilot must log the following time (61.51):
  - Training & aeronautical experience to meet the requirements for a certificate, rating, or flight review
  - The aeronautical experience required for currency
- With regard to the required log, the following must be included:
  - Conditions of flight (day, night, actual instrument, simulated instrument)
  - Date
  - Total flight time or total lesson time
  - Locations
  - Type & ID of aircraft or sim / FTD
  - Name of safety pilot
  - Type of experience (solo, PIC, SIC, flight / ground training received, training received in a sim / FTD)
- Though not a 61.51 required item, log takeoffs & landings to demonstrate meeting currency requirements
- Falsification of a logbook or any document used to show compliance for obtaining a certificate, rating, or authorization, or any requirement to exercise the privileges of the certificate, may result in the suspension or revocation of any certificate, rating, or authorization
- Student pilots must carry their logbook on any flight that they are the PIC

Aircraft Logbooks

- Review a sample set of aircraft logbooks with the student
- (Excerpt from 43.11) The person approving or disapproving for return to service an aircraft, airframe, aircraft engine, propeller, appliance, or component part after any inspection performed in accordance with the appropriate regulations shall make an entry in the maintenance record of that equipment containing the following information:
  - The type of inspection and a brief description of the extent of the inspection
  - The date of the inspection and aircraft total time in service
  - The signature, the certificate number, and kind of certificate held by the person
  - A statement regarding the airworthiness or unairworthiness of the aircraft

Practical Test Standards

- Review the Practical Test Standards section of the *PTS Study Guide* with the student
- Ensure that the student understands that these are the goals that he will be working toward during the course of training
- Ensure that he understands how the DVD cross-reference works

Advisory Circulars

- The FAA provides guidance through Advisory Circulars (AC)
- ACs are nonregulatory
  - They explain or amplify information in the FARs or procedures that require detailed explanation because of questions from the field, accidents, incidents, or for other reasons
- Unless they are incorporated into a regulation by reference, ACs are not legally binding, but they should be heeded
- The first two numbers in an AC id relate to the applicable part of the regulations
  - The numbers and letters that follow the series number identify the publication and version

LESSON G2 – AIRPORTS

Note to Instructor

- Review the student's personal minimums checklist from lesson G1

Wind Direction Indicators

- A wind cone, wind sock, or wind tee may be installed near the operational runway to indicate wind direction
  - The large end of the wind cone / wind sock points into the wind as does the large end (cross bar) of the wind tee

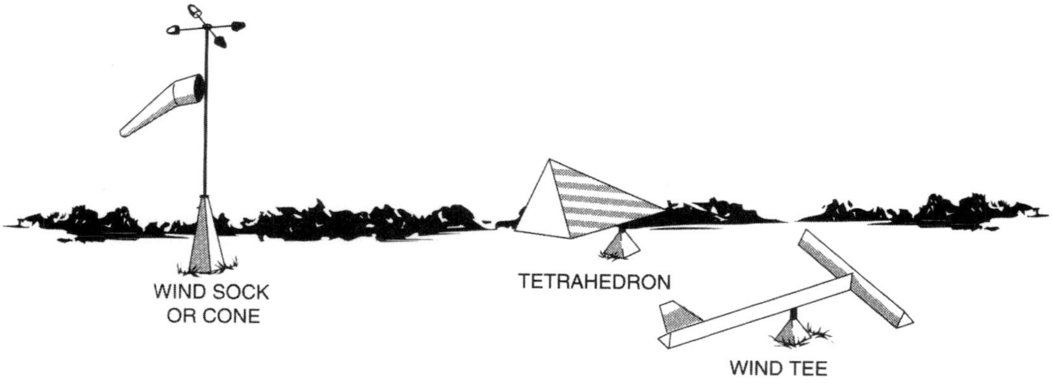

Figure 2-1. – Runway wind direction indicators.

- Pilots are cautioned against using a tetrahedron to indicate wind direction
  - The tetrahedron typically points into the wind and indicates the landing direction but may be ineffective in light winds
- The wind direction indicator is often located within a segmented circle that is designed to provide traffic pattern information
  - Landing strip indicators are installed in pairs and used to show the alignment of landing strips
  - Traffic pattern indicators are arranged in pairs in conjunction with landing strip indicators and used to indicate the direction of turns when there is a variation from the normal left traffic pattern

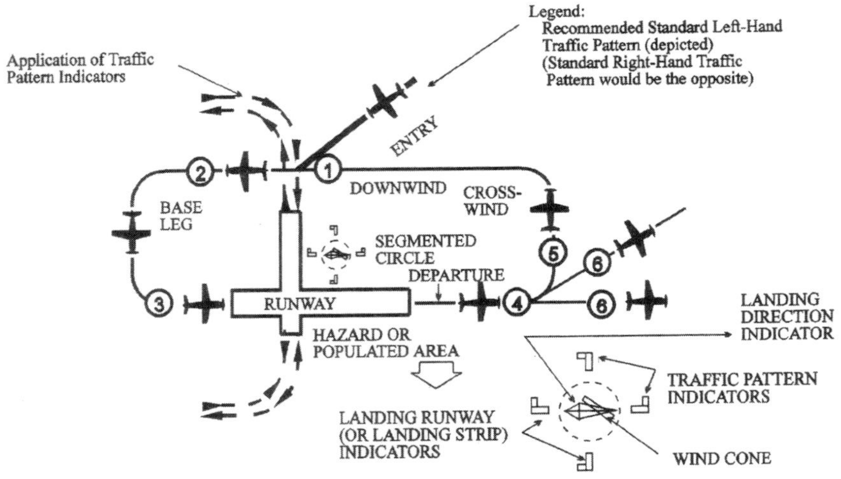

Figure 2-2. – Traffic pattern procedures and legs.

- Traffic patterns are designed to provide standardization so that everyone knows what to expect

- Traffic pattern legs
  - Entry
  - Upwind
  - Crosswind
  - Downwind
  - Base
  - Final
  - Departure
- Radio calls in the pattern should be made when entering a new leg

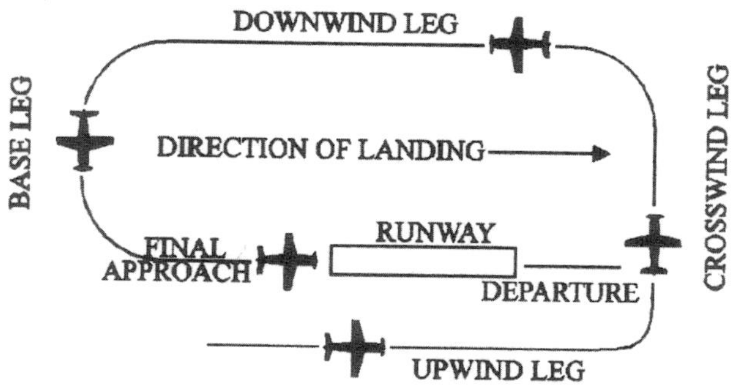

Figure 2-3. – Traffic pattern legs.

- DON'T expect everyone to always fly standard patterns or use the radio!

Airport, Runway, and Taxiway Signs

- Review AIM Chapter 2, Section 3 and other training aids with the student
- Airport Signs – color is key
  - Red – mandatory
  - Black / yellow letters – position
  - Yellow – directional

Figure 2-4. – Example of a directional sign.

Airport, Runway, and Taxiway Markings

- Review AIM Chapter 2, Section 3 and other training aids with the student

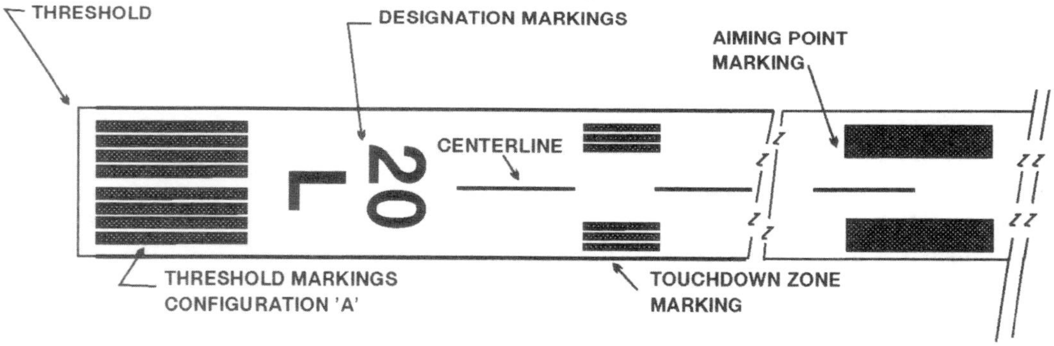

Figure 2-5. – Examples of runway markings.

- Ensure that the student understands that runway numbering is based on magnetic heading

Airport, Runway, and Taxiway Lighting

- Review AIM Chapter 2, Section 1 with the student
- Ensure that the student understands VASIs and PAPIs along with other lighting

Radio Calls and Checks

- Review AIM Chapter 4, Section 2 with the student
- Emphasis should be placed on listening and thinking before transmitting, order of wording, the phonetic alphabet, numbers, altitudes, and directions

- Use the "4 W's"
  - Who you're calling
  - Who you are
  - Where you are
  - What your intentions are
  - Add who you're calling on the end for clarification when appropriate

CTAF

- The CTAF (Common Traffic Advisory Frequency) is a frequency designed for the purpose of carrying out airport advisory practices while operating to or from an airport without an operating control tower
- The CTAF may be a UNICOM, Multicom, FSS, or tower frequency (when closed) and is identified in appropriate aeronautical publications
  - UNICOM – A nongovernment communication facility which may provide airport information at certain airports
  - Multicom – A mobile service not open to public correspondence used to provide communications essential to conduct the activities being performed by or directed from private aircraft
  - Flight Service Station (FSS) – Air traffic facilities which provide
    - Pilot briefing
    - En route communications
    - VFR search and rescue services
    - Assist lost aircraft and aircraft in emergency situations
    - Relay ATC clearances
    - Originate Notices to Airmen
    - Broadcast aviation weather and NAS information
    - Receive and process IFR flight plans
    - Monitor NAVAIDs
  - In addition, at selected locations, FSSs provide
    - En Route Flight Advisory Service (Flight Watch)
    - Take weather observations
    - Issue airport advisories
    - Advise Customs and Immigration of trans–border flights

Obtaining Airport Advisories

- A Local Airport Advisory is a service provided by flight service stations or the military at airports not serviced by an operating control tower
  - This service consists of providing information to arriving and departing aircraft concerning wind direction and speed, favored runway, altimeter setting, pertinent known traffic, pertinent known field conditions, airport taxi routes and traffic patterns, and authorized instrument approach procedures
    - This information is advisory in nature and does not constitute an ATC clearance
- Other Airport Advisories common at non–tower airports may be obtained over the CTAF from traffic in the pattern or through the UNICOM

- Pilots landing at non-tower airports should begin monitoring the CTAF at least 10-20 miles out from the airport, if practical, to attempt to learn the information required
  - If unable to determine the required information, an airport advisory should be requested at least 5-10 miles out from the airport
- Review the phraseology for an airport advisory radio call with the student

Runway Incursions

- Aircraft, vehicles, people or equipment going onto an active runway in such a way as to create a collision hazard
- The potential for runway incursions can be reduced through adequate planning, coordination, and communication
- Knowledge and situational awareness are the keys to prevention
- Never taxi onto any runway without first looking for traffic landing on or using that runway
- Always monitor the CTAF and/or appropriate ATC frequencies while operating on the surface of an airport

Collision Avoidance

- At non-towered airports and while flying en route, the pilot alone is responsible for avoiding mid-air collisions!
- Even at towered airports and under ATC control, the pilot should "back up" the controller by practicing good collision avoidance techniques
- Eyes are best defense against a mid-air collision
  - Look outside the aircraft
  - Use the radio
    - Don't expect everyone else to use their radios
- Pilots should also be familiar with the following information to reduce the possibility of mid-air collisions
  - Determine relative altitude using the horizon as a reference point
  - Take Appropriate Action
    - Pilots must be familiar with rules on right-of-way, so if an aircraft is on an obvious collision course, one can take immediate evasive action, preferably in compliance with applicable Federal Aviation Regulations
  - Consider Multiple Threats
    - The decision to climb, descend, or turn is a matter of personal judgment, but one should anticipate that the other pilot may also be making a quick maneuver
      - Watch the other aircraft during the maneuver and begin scanning again immediately since there may be other aircraft in the area
  - Collision Course Targets
    - Any aircraft that appears to have no relative motion and stays in one scan quadrant is likely to be on a collision course
  - Recognize High Hazard Areas – Airports and airways, especially near VOR's, are places where aircraft tend to cluster

- Cockpit Management – Studying maps, checklists, and manuals before flight, with other proper preflight planning, can reduce the amount of time required to look at these items during flight, permitting more scan time
- Windshield Conditions – Dirty or bug-smeared windshields can greatly reduce the ability of pilots to see other aircraft
- Visibility Conditions – Smoke, haze, dust, rain, and flying towards the sun can also greatly reduce the ability to detect targets
- Visual Obstructions in the Cockpit – Pilots need to move their heads to see around blind spots caused by fixed aircraft structures, such as door posts, wings, etc.
- Lights On – Day or night, use of exterior lights can greatly increase the conspicuity of any aircraft
- ATC Support – ATC facilities often provide radar traffic advisories on a workload-permitting basis
- Check Blind Spots – Wings and posts can hide other aircraft

Scanning for Traffic

- Scanning the sky for other aircraft is a key factor in collision avoidance
- Pilots must develop an effective scanning technique which maximizes one's visual capabilities
- While the eyes can observe an approximate 200 degree arc of the horizon at one glance, only a very small center area called the fovea, in the rear of the eye, has the ability to send clear, sharply focused messages to the brain
  - An aircraft at a distance of 7 miles which appears in sharp focus within the foveal center of vision would have to be as close as 7/10 of a mile in order to be recognized if it were outside of foveal vision
- Because the eyes can focus only on this narrow viewing area, effective scanning is accomplished with a series of short, regularly spaced eye movements that bring successive areas of the sky into the central visual field
  - Each movement should not exceed 10 degrees, and each area should be observed for at least 1 second to enable detection
- Pilots should realize that their eyes may require several seconds to refocus when switching views between items in the cockpit and distant objects
  - The eyes will also tire more quickly when forced to adjust to distances immediately after close-up focus, as required for scanning the instrument panel
  - Eye fatigue can be reduced by looking from the instrument panel to a wing, past the wing tip, to the center of the first scan quadrant when beginning the exterior scan
  - After having scanned the exterior, allow the eyes to return to the cabin along the other wing from its tip inward
  - Once back inside, one should commence the panel scan
- Effective scanning also helps avoid "empty-field myopia"
  - This condition usually occurs when flying above the clouds or in a haze layer that provides nothing specific to focus on outside the aircraft
  - This causes the eyes to relax and seek a comfortable focal distance which may range from 10 to 30 feet

LESSON G3 – AERODYNAMICS

4 Forces of Flight

- Lift
  - Supporting force for flight in an atmosphere
  - Acts perpendicular to the relative wind
  - Generated through Bernoulli's Principle and Newton's Laws
  - Discuss leading edge, trailing edge, chord line, relative wind, camber, camber line, stagnation point, and angle of attack

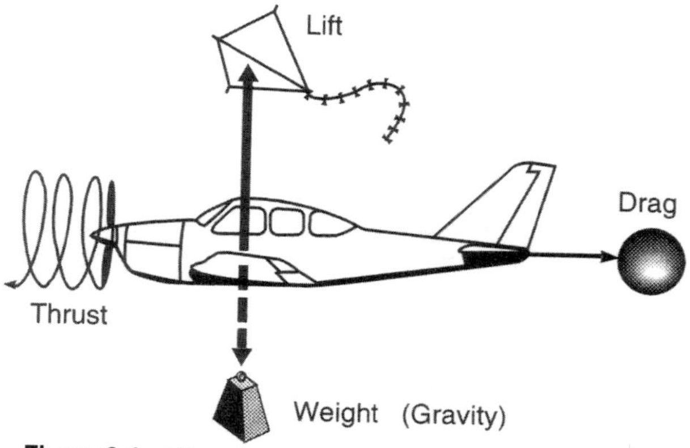

Figure 3-1. – Four forces acting on an aircraft in flight.

- Thrust
  - Considered to act parallel and just about on the Longitudinal axis
  - Produced by movement of the air by propeller or expansion of air in a turbine
- Weight
  - Mass x Acceleration (Gravity)
  - Always acts towards the center of the Earth
  - Considered to act from the Center of Gravity
    - CG is the point on the aircraft, that if suspended, it would balance
- Drag
  - Two Types – Parasite & Induced
  - Retarding force
  - Acts parallel to the relative wind
- During Straight & Level
  - Lift = Weight (and tail down force)
  - Thrust = Drag
- Other circumstances of steady state flight
  - Upward acting forces are equal to downward forces
  - Forward forces = retarding forces

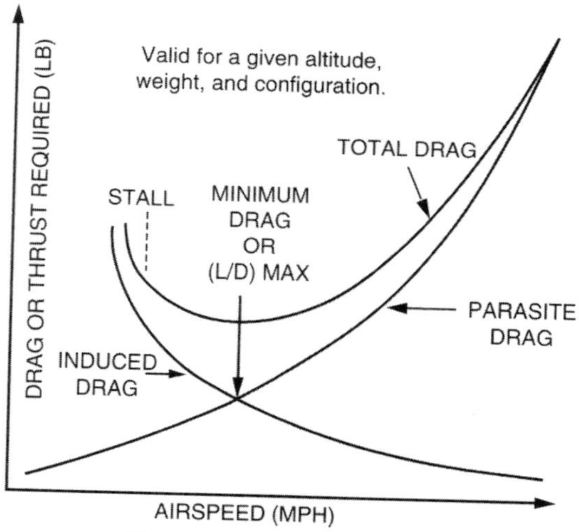

Figure 3-2. – Types of drag.

Airframe Construction (Components)

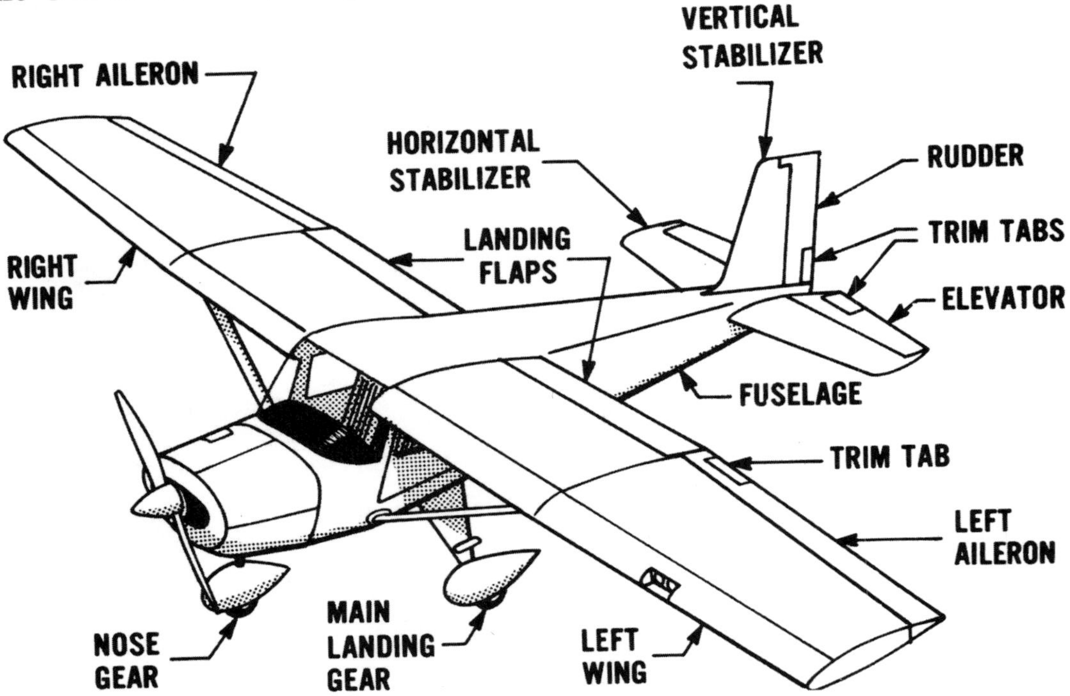

Figure 3-3. – Parts of an airplane.

- Fuselage
  - Monocoque Construction – Skin carries all of the stress
  - Truss Construction – Internal structure with a non-load carrying skin
  - Semi-Monocoque – Combination, inside formers & stringers carry some of the structure
- Wings
  - Provide lift that supports the aircraft in flight
  - Full Cantilever – Internal support structure, no external bracing
    - Internal bracing of the wing – ribs, spar, stringers, leading edge "D" cell, wing root, & wing tip
  - Semi-Cantilever – Some external bracing, compression & tension
- Empennage (Tail Group)
  - Vertical Stabilizer – Provides directional balance
  - Rudder – Controls direction of yaw
  - Horizontal Stabilizer – Longitudinal balance
  - Elevator (Stabilator) – Controls the pitch
- Flight Controls
  - Primary Flight Controls
    - Rudder – Yaw about the vertical axis
    - Elevator – Pitch about the lateral axis
    - Ailerons – Bank (Roll) around the longitudinal axis

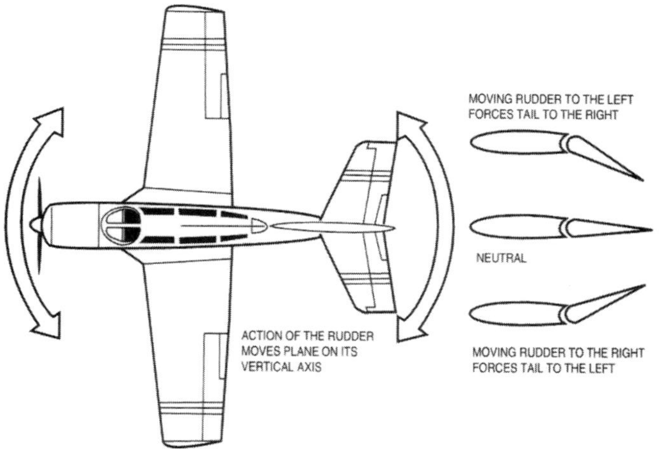

Figure 3-4. – Effects of the rudder on the aircraft.

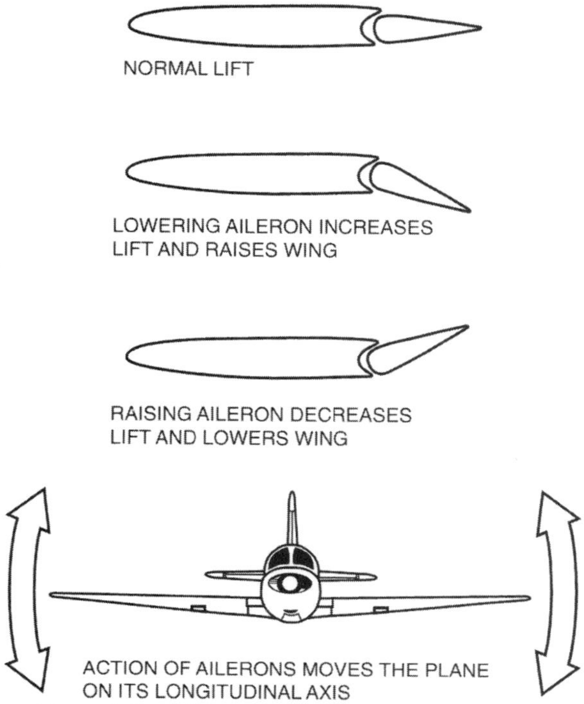

Figure 3-5. – Effects of the ailerons on the aircraft.

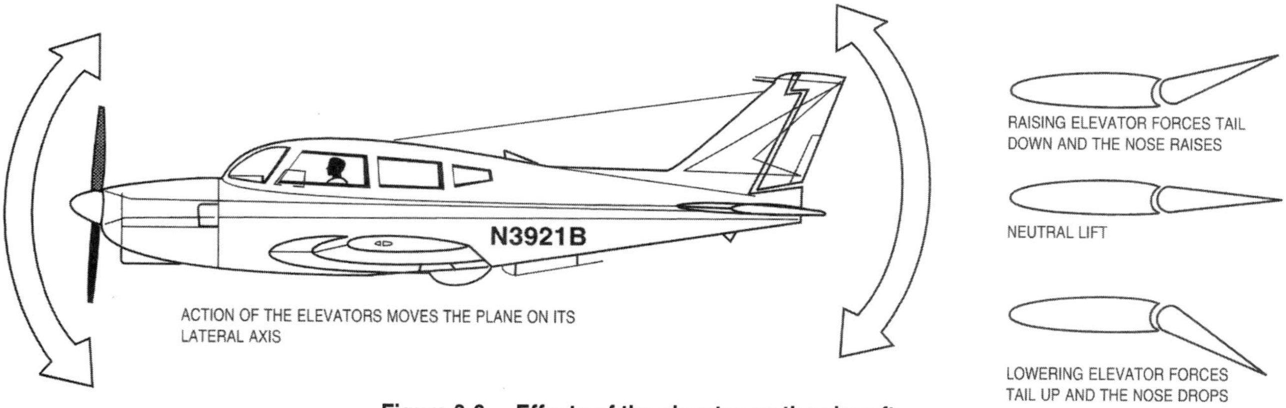

Figure 3-6. – Effects of the elevator on the aircraft.

- Secondary Flight Controls
  - Trim Tabs – Used in trimming & balancing the aircraft
    - Trim Tabs
    - Servo Tabs
    - Balance Tabs
    - Anti-Servo Tabs
  - Spoilers & Dive Brakes – Increase descent without an increase in speed
  - Wing Flaps
    - Plain
    - Split
    - Slotted
    - Fowler

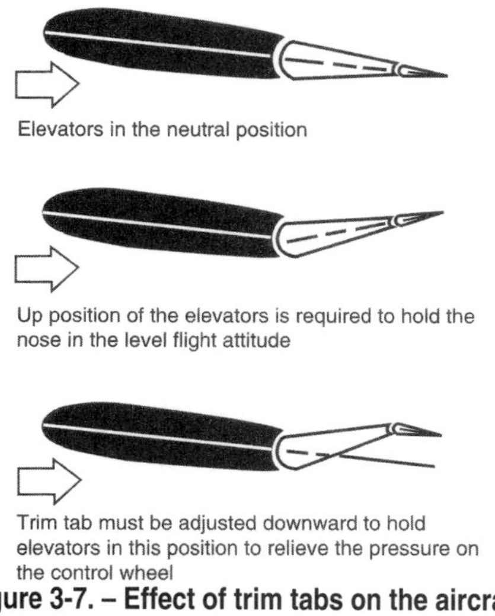

Figure 3-7. – Effect of trim tabs on the aircraft.

- Landing Gear
  - Retractable vs. Fixed
  - Tricycle vs. Conventional
    - Discuss advantages and disadvantages of each
  - Types
    - Spring
    - Strut (piston)
    - Rubber shock donut
  - Brakes
    - Stopping
    - Hold for run up
    - Steering
  - Steering
    - Rudder pedal linkage
    - Wheel (tiller)
    - Switch

Three Axes of Flight

- Lateral Axis – Wingtip to Wingtip
- Longitudinal Axis – Nose to Tail
- Vertical Axis – Straight up through the body at the junction of Lateral & Longitudinal
- All meet at Center of Gravity

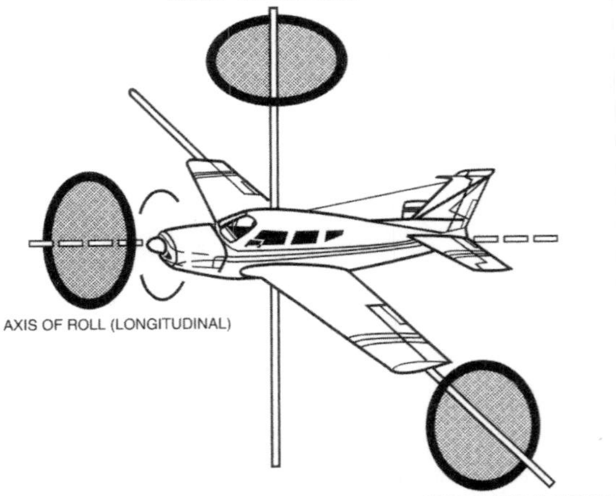

Figure 3-8. – Three axes of the aircraft.

Forces Acting on a Climbing Aircraft

- Direction of flight is away from the Earth
- Different types
  - V_Y – Best Rate
    - Most altitude per unit of time
  - V_X – Best Angle
    - Most altitude per unit of distance
  - Cruise Climb
    - Used for improved cooling & visibility
- Steady State Climb (Constant Rate & Airspeed Climb)
  - Lift is greater for the entry
    - Stabilized
  - Lift may be about the same
    - Remember it is acting parallel to the relative wind
  - Weight is the same
    - Portion is acting in the same direction as drag
  - Thrust
    - Supporting drag and a component of weight

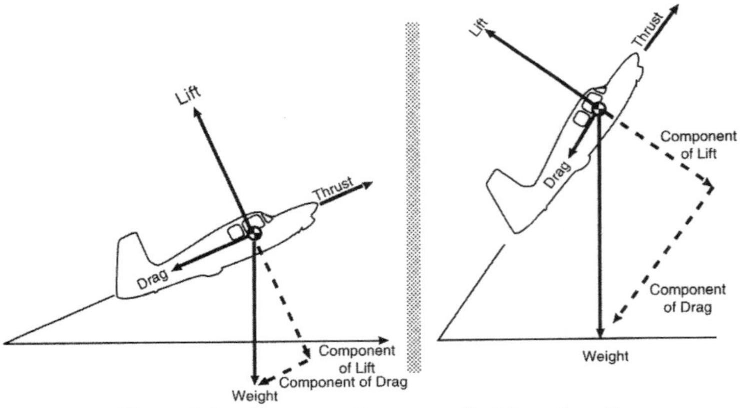

Figure 3-9. – Forces acting on a climbing aircraft.

- Torque Effect
  - P-Factor
    - Descending propeller blade produces more lift (thrust), while the aircraft is at a high angle of attack, creating yaw
  - Torque Reaction
    - Twisting of engine creates roll & yaw
  - Spiraling Slipstream
    - Twisting air around fuselage creates yaw & roll
  - Gyroscopic Precession
    - Propeller acts as gyroscope

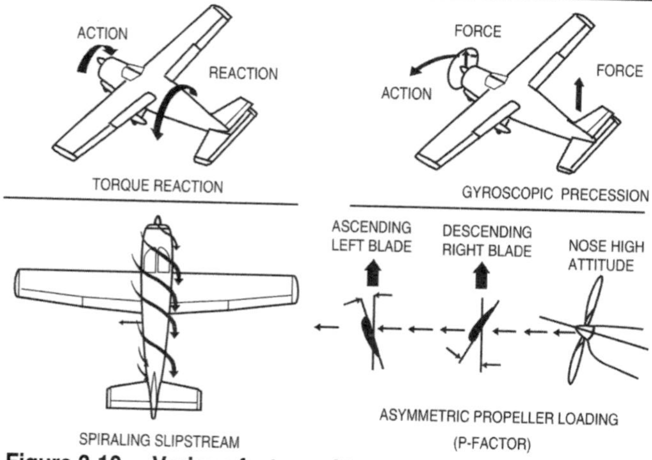

Figure 3-10. – Various factors of torque acting on the aircraft.

Forces Acting on a Descending Airplane

- Lift
  - May be the same as level
- Thrust
  - Pilot's prerogative
- Weight
  - Component acts along the same direction as Thrust
- Drag
  - May go up
- Best glide
  - Most distance per unit of altitude
  - Review for current training aircraft

Forces Acting on a Turning Airplane

- Bank the aircraft in order to change the direction of flight
  - Rudder yaws but does not create the unbalance of forces needed to change direction
    - Slip – tail inside
    - Skid – tail outside
- Adverse Yaw
  - Yawing moment opposite the direction of turn
  - Bad because of added drag
  - Corrections
    - Proper rudder usage
    - Frise type ailerons
    - Differential ailerons
    - Use of spoilers to bank the aircraft

- Horizontal Turns
  - Lift vector is tilted
    - Creates an acceleration
  - Lift
    - Vertical = Lift x Cosine Angle of Bank (AOB)
    - Horizontal = Lift X Sine AOB
- Types of Turns
  - Shallow Bank – 0° to 20°
  - Medium Bank – 20° to 45°
  - Steep Bank – More than 45°
- Level Turns
  - Vertical = Weight
  - Horizontal is called centripetal force
  - G's are the acceleration
    - Combination of acceleration sideways & down

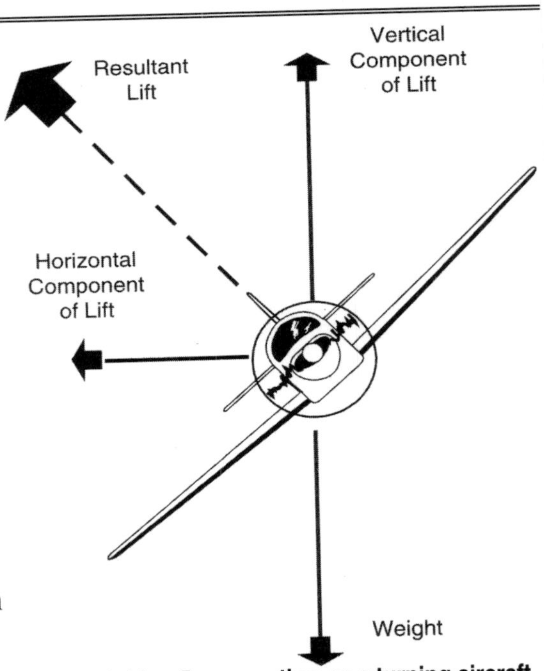

Figure 3-11. – Forces acting on a turning aircraft.

Effects of Flaps

- Extending the flaps increases:
  - Wing camber
  - Wing area (some types)
  - Angle of attack of the wing
- These changes increase lift and drag (induced and parasite)
- Allows pilot to make a steeper approach without increasing airspeed
- May provide increased lift required for certain maneuvers

LESSON G4 – AIRPLANE STABILITY, LOAD FACTORS, & WAKE TURBULENCE

Static Stability (Positive / Negative)

- Stability is the inherent quality of an airplane to correct for conditions that may disturb it from equilibrium
- Static stability is the initial tendency of the aircraft's reaction to the disturbance from equilibrium
  - An aircraft with positive static stability will tend to react in the direction back toward equilibrium when disturbed
  - An aircraft with neutral static stability will tend to stay in the direction that the disturbance has taken it
  - An aircraft with negative static stability will tend to continue further from equilibrium when disturbed

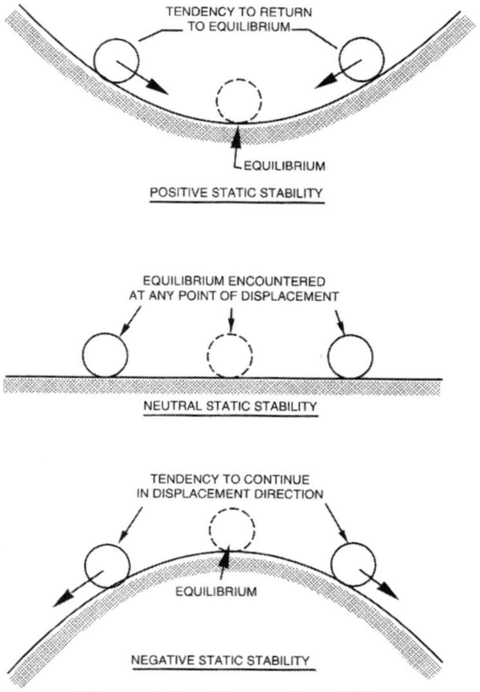

Figure 4-1. – Types of stability.

Dynamic Stability (Positive / Negative)

- Dynamic stability is the result which occurs over time when reacting to a disturbance from equilibrium
- Dynamic stability requires positive static stability as the initial reaction
  - An aircraft with positive dynamic stability will tend to return to equilibrium through smaller and smaller oscillations
  - An aircraft with neutral dynamic stability will tend to continue oscillating with the same magnitude for each oscillation
  - An aircraft with negative dynamic stability will tend to continue oscillating with the magnitude of each oscillation increasing

Dihedral Effect

- Dihedral is the angle at which the wings are slanted upward from the root to the tip
- Dihedral's stabilizing effect is the result of a slight sideslip which occurs when one wing is forced down
  - The sideslip creates a difference between the angle of attack (AOA) on the upper and lower wings with the lower wing having a greater AOA and tending to raise this wing

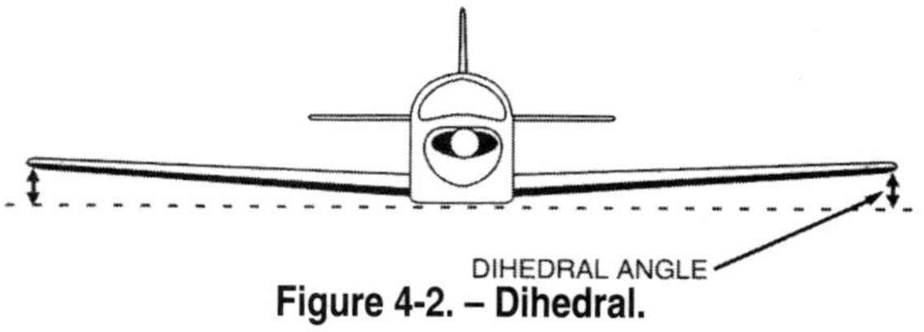

Figure 4-2. – Dihedral.

Ground Effect

- A condition of improved performance encountered when the aircraft is operated near the ground
  - The ground changes the airflow around the wing by restricting the vertical component
    - This reduces the upwash, downwash, & wingtip vortices
    - Results in a reduction of induced drag
- Uses and dangers of ground effect
  - Good stuff
    - Allows the pilot to reduce wear and tear on the aircraft and increase acceleration when operating from a soft-field
    - May be utilized to soften a landing
  - Bad stuff
    - May allow the aircraft to takeoff before the aircraft is ready to continue flying which can result in settling

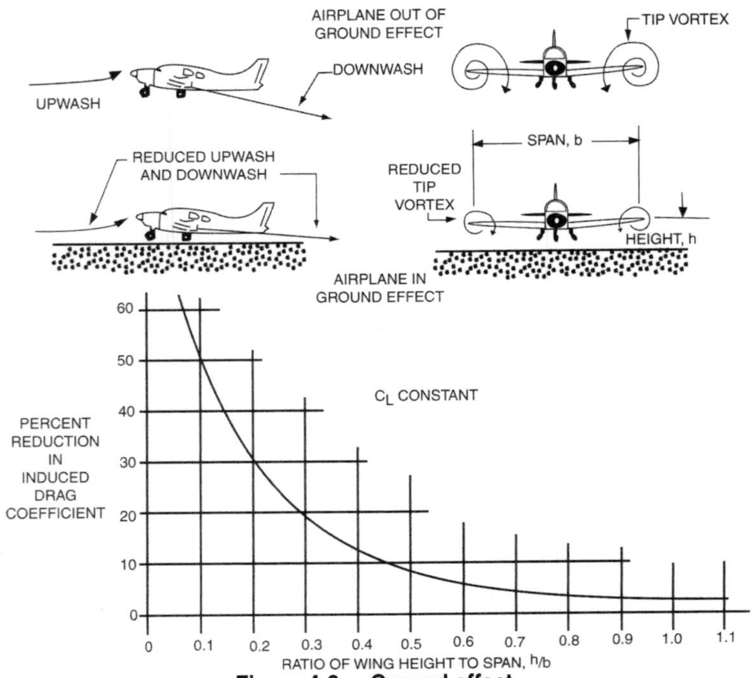

Figure 4-3. – Ground effect.

- May cause excessive float on landing

Wing Tip Vortices

- All flying airplanes create a wake off of their wingtips (rotors)
  - Air slipping from the higher pressure below the wing to the lower pressure above creates a swirling trail behind the aircraft

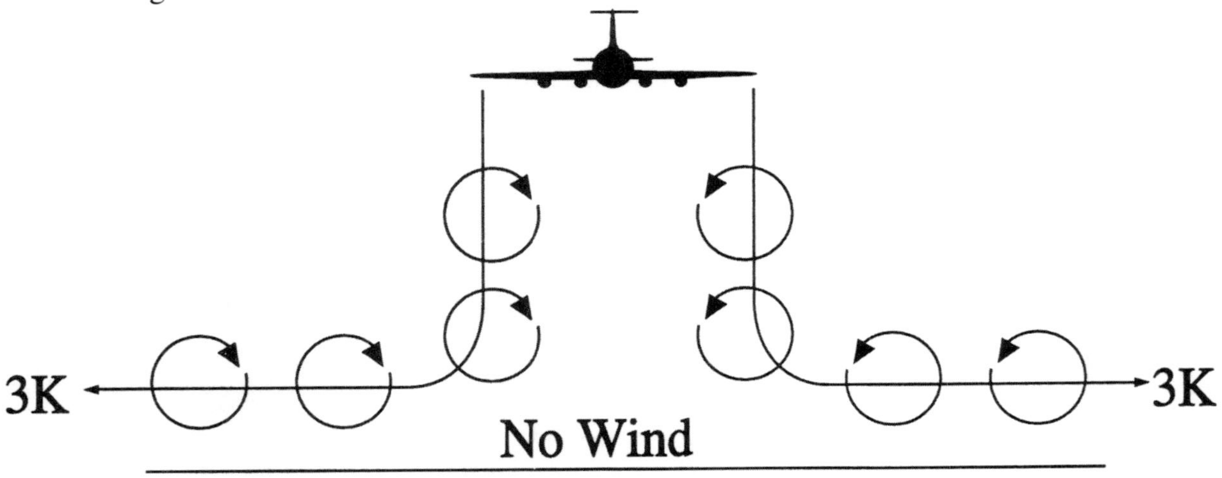

Figure 4-4. – Vortex movement near ground – no wind.

Wake Turbulence & Avoidance

- Wing tip vortices are the primary source of wake turbulence and contribute to induced drag
- Strongest wake
  - Heavy (larger AOA)
  - Clean (no abrupt changes in the wing)
  - Slow (large AOA)
- Another type of wake turbulence is jet blast
  - The exhaust from a jet can easily flip a light aircraft
  - Stay back 500 feet
- Wake turbulence avoidance in flight
  - Avoid 5+ miles behind the aircraft
  - Avoid 1,000 feet below the aircraft
- Wake turbulence avoidance during landing
  - Approach above the larger aircraft's path
    - Even if a crossing path
  - Touchdown beyond the larger aircraft touchdown point
  - Land prior to larger aircraft's rotation point
  - Be cautious of crosswinds that can make wake turbulence drift
- Wake turbulence avoidance while departing
  - Rotate prior to and climb above the larger aircraft's flight path
  - Wait 2-3 minutes if departing to allow the turbulence to dissipate

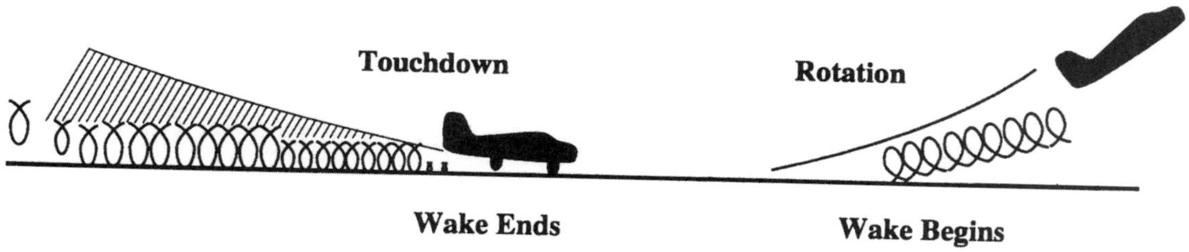

Figure 4-5. – Wake turbulence on takeoff and landing.

Load Factor & Gusts

- A load is a force which is supported by the wings of the aircraft
  - The load in straight-and-level, unaccelerated flight is the weight of the aircraft and its contents
- A load factor is a ratio of the total load supported by the wings to the actual weight of the aircraft and its contents
  - Also referred to as "G's" (gravities)
- In straight-and-level, unaccelerated flight, the load factor is 1 G
- Maneuvers such as pulling up into a climb or turning the airplane will increase the G load
- The load factor in a coordinated, level-flight turn may be determined by the bank angle of the turning aircraft

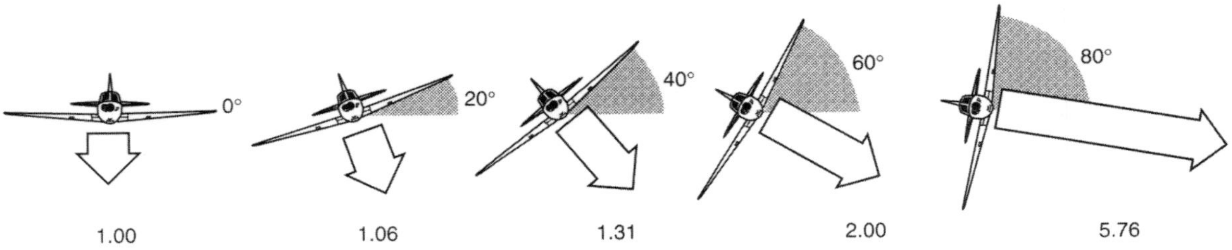

Figure 4-6. – Increase of load factor as bank increases.

- In order to maintain level-flight during a turn, the wings must produce enough lift to support the weight of the aircraft multiplied by the load factor
- The increased angle of attack required to produce the extra lift at any given bank angle will increase the stall speed of the airplane
  - Multiply the straight-and-level stall speed by the square-root of the load factor to determine the higher stall speed
- The aircraft was designed to handle a certain load factor without breaking
  - Normal = +2.5 to +3.8/-1.0 to -1.52 (range is weight dependent)
  - Utility = +4.4/-1.76
  - Acrobatic = +6.0/-3.0
  - Transport = +2.5 to +3.8/-1.0 (range is weight dependent)
- If the aircraft experiences a higher load while still above the stall speed for that load factor, damage or complete failure may result
  - A stall will tend to relieve the load and prevent damage
  - V_A (design maneuvering speed) is the maximum speed at which the aircraft will stall before a damaging load factor results
    - Another definition for V_A: The maximum speed at which full or abrupt control movements may be used without overstressing the airframe
  - V_A changes with the weight of the aircraft and its contents
- Vertical air currents or gusts may impose an increased load factor on an airplane
  - These gusts are felt by the pilot and passengers as turbulence
  - The aircraft's speed must be kept below V_{NO} in any turbulence to prevent damage
    - It should be kept below V_A in severe or greater turbulence to allow an additional safety factor

LESSON G5 – AIRCRAFT PERFORMANCE

Factors Affecting Performance

- Additional ***weight*** has the following performance effects:
  - Higher takeoff speed
  - Longer takeoff run
  - Reduced rate & angle of climb
  - Higher landing speed
  - Longer landing roll
- ***Wind*** is like extra or less airspeed depending upon the conditions
  - Headwind – decrease takeoff & landing distance
  - Tailwind – Increase takeoff & landing distance
  - Crosswind – Increase takeoff & landing distance
- Runway Surface Condition
  - The friction of the landing surface plays a major factor – More friction usually means *longer* takeoff rolls and *shorter* landing rolls
  - Gravel & "farmer's mix" pavement may cause longer takeoff & landing rolls
- Runway Gradient
  - Upslope – increase takeoff roll & decrease landing roll distances
  - Downslope – decrease takeoff roll & increase landing roll distances
  - All other conditions being the same it is preferred to takeoff downhill & land going uphill
- Density Altitude & Humidity
  - The less dense the air is, the less performance from the aircraft
    - The engine produces less power
    - The propeller is less efficient
    - The wing is less efficient
  - Density Altitude is calculated based on the following:
    - Pressure
    - Temperature
  - High Density Altitude
    - Low density of the air (like being at a high altitude)
  - Low Density Altitude
    - High air density (like being at a low altitude)
  - Humidity
    - A water vapor molecule has less mass than N_2 or O_2 molecule therefore the air is less dense when humid
    - Usually not accounted for in calculations...but beware of its effects

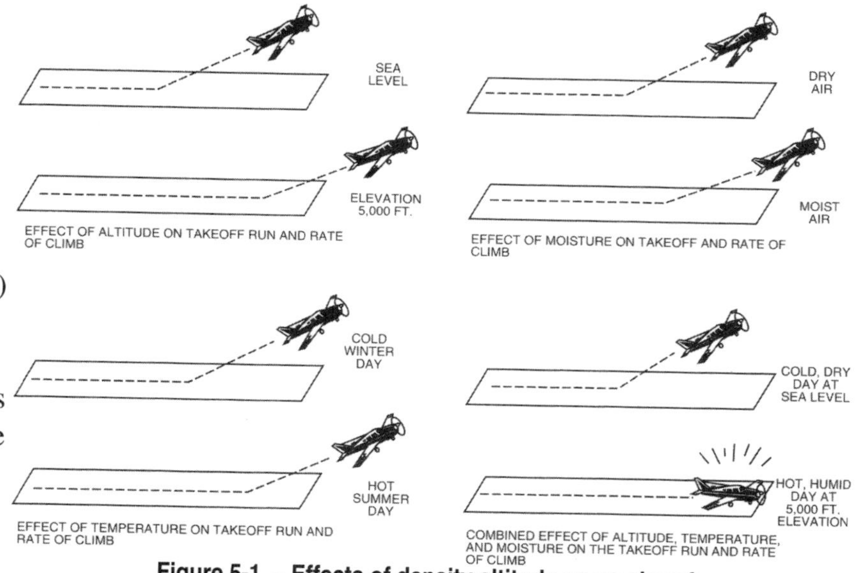

Figure 5-1. – Effects of density altitude on an aircraft.

- Pilot Technique
  - How the pilot flies the aircraft can greatly affect the distance of the takeoff & landing rolls

Takeoff Data Card

- Contains convenient place for all performance calculations
- Required for commercial airline operations

Aircraft Weight & Balance			
N______	Limits: (Fore/Aft) ______ / ______		
Index: 10 100 1000	Weight	Arm	Moment
Basic Empty Weight			
Pilot & Passenger			
Rear Passengers Station 1			
Rear Passengers Station 2			
Baggage			
Zero Fuel Weight			
Fuel (6 PPG)			
Ramp Weight			
Start/Taxi/Run up			
Takeoff Weight			
Load Adjustments: Passenger			
Load Adjustments: Baggage			
Load Adjustments: Fuel			
Adjusted Takeoff Weight			
Fuel Burn			
Landing Weight			

Aircraft Performance Data					
Takeoff Distance	Normal______		50' Obstacle______		
Landing Distance	Normal______		50' Obstacle______		
V_{s0}		V_y		V_{ne}	
V_s		V_{le}		Best Glide	
V_{fe}		V_{lo}		App. Speed	
V_x		V_a		Endurance	___H___M
RPM/MP		GPH		TAS	
Active Runway					
Windspeed & Direction					
Crosswind Component					
Pressure Altitude					
Density Altitude					
Frequencies:					

Figure 5-2. – Takeoff data card.

Aircraft Weight and Balance

- Failure to compute an appropriate weight and balance could result in injury or death
- 14 CFR 91.103 (b)(2) – "...other reliable information appropriate to the aircraft, relating to aircraft performance under expected values of airport elevation and runway slope, aircraft gross weight, and wind and temperature"
- Adverse effects of overloaded aircraft
  - Higher takeoff speed
  - Longer takeoff run
  - Reduced rate & angle of climb
  - Lower maximum altitude
  - Shorter range
  - Lower cruise speed
  - Less maneuverability
  - Higher stall speeds
  - Higher landing speed
  - Longer landing roll
  - Additional stress on landing gear & structure
- Primary concerns
  - Gross weight – Too much and the aircraft may not fly
  - Forward or aft CG
    - Forward – Degraded cruise & climb performance and more difficult to rotate & flare due to larger taildown force requirement
    - Aft – Better cruise performance, less stability, difficulty in recovering from stalls

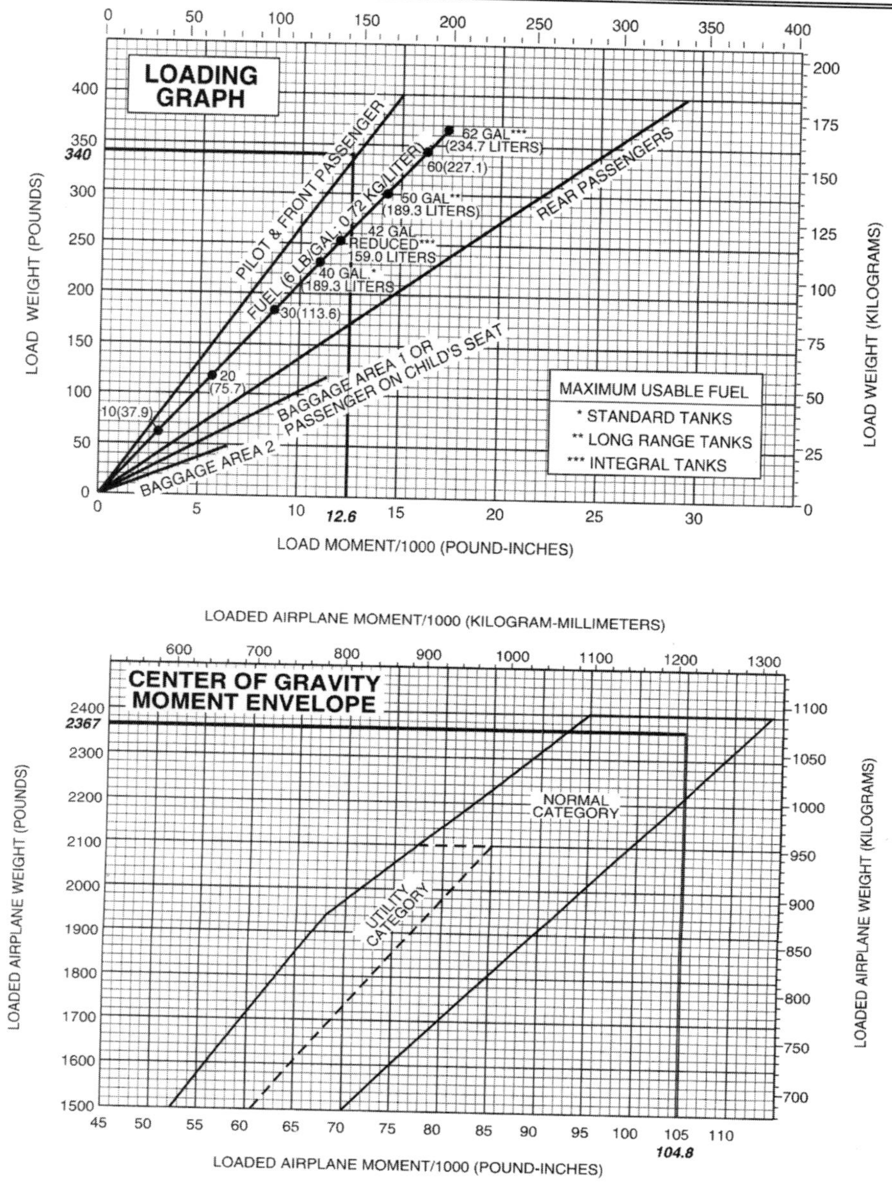

Figure 5-3. – Sample weight and balance graphs.

➢ Important Terms

- Arm – Horizontal distance of an item from datum
- C.G. – The point that the aircraft would balance
- Datum – Reference line for arm measurements
- Moment – Weight x Arm
- Station – Location designated by arm
- Useful Load – Weight carrying capability
- Empty Weight – Aircraft w/ equipment, ballast, hydraulic fluid, undrainable oil & unusable fuel
    - Basic Empty Weight – Full oil
- Max Gross Weight – Maximum weight of the aircraft at anytime
- Maximum Takeoff – Maximum weight of the aircraft for takeoff
- Maximum Landing – Maximum weight of the aircraft for landing

- Useful weights
  - Gas – 6# / gal
  - Oil – 7.5# / gal (1.875# / quart)
  - Jet – 6.7# / gal
- Work through a number of sample problems with the student
- Equipment List
  - Review the equipment list for the training aircraft with the student

Basic Performance Charts

- Review the performance charts for the training aircraft with the student
- Work through several practice problems ensuring that the student understands the impact of density altitude factors

Headwind / Crosswind Calculations

- Need to determine the angle between the runway & wind direction
  - If the wind direction is variable use the largest angle
  - Remember that printed wind directions are *true* direction & runway orientation is *magnetic*
    - Add or subtract variation as required
- Variable winds
  - If the speed of the wind is variable
    - If focusing on headwind component use the lowest wind speed
    - If focusing on crosswind component use the highest wind speed
    - If focusing on both equally use the mean (average) wind speed
- Ways to do it
  - Graph
  - E6B flight computer
    - Electronic
    - Manual
  - Mathematically

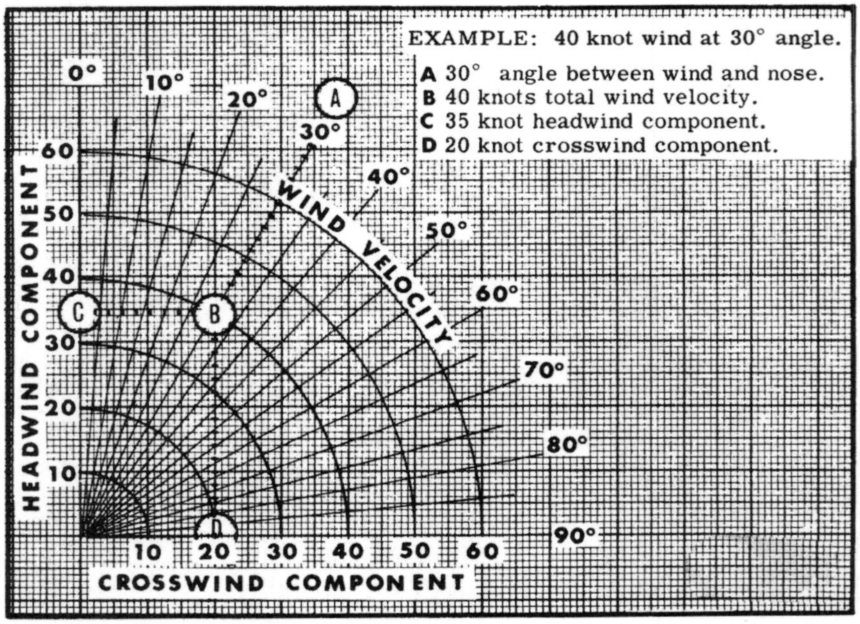

Figure 5-4. – Crosswind component chart.

LESSON G6 – WEATHER

The Atmosphere

- Earth is surrounded by a thin layer of air
  - Air is composed of oxygen, nitrogen, carbon dioxide, and trace elements of other gases
  - Air also contains evaporated water
    - Water vapor is directly involved in all weather phenomena
- 50% of Earth's atmosphere is contained below 18,000'
- Parts of the Atmosphere
  - Troposphere – portion of atmosphere from the surface up to 5-10 miles
    - On average, the temperature decreases about 2° C for every 1,000' up
      - This is called the "standard lapse rate"
    - Cooling is due to decreased air pressure
  - Tropopause is a thin layer with a sudden decrease in temperature lapse rate
    - Acts as a lid for water vapor
    - Thin division between troposphere and stratosphere
    - Confines most weather phenomena to the troposphere
  - Stratosphere
    - Layer of air above the tropopause
    - Extends from tropopause to 160,000'
    - Very little temperature change with altitude
  - Troposphere and stratosphere are where most flight takes place

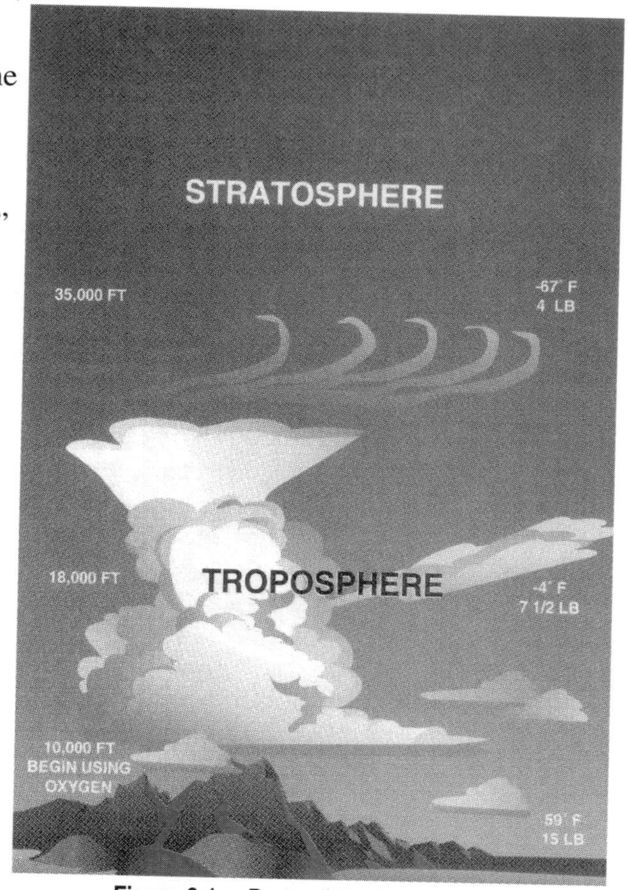

Figure 6-1. – Parts of the atmosphere.

- Causes of Weather
  - Every physical process of weather is accompanied by, or is the result of, heat exchanges
  - Unequal heating of earth's surface causes differences in pressure
  - Wind is the flow of air from areas of high pressure to areas of low pressure
  - Tendency of the atmosphere is to flow from the poles to the equator, heat up, rise and flow back to the poles
  - Coriolis force deflects wind to the right (northern hemisphere)
  - Surface friction also influences wind flow

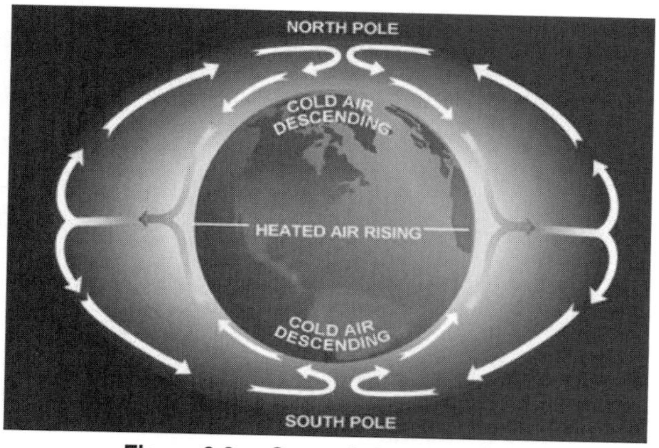

Figure 6-2. – General global air flow.

- Coriolis Force
  - Force caused by spinning of the earth
  - Varies in strength with latitude
  - Zero at equator
  - Strongest at poles
  - Responsible for changing north-south tendency of atmosphere into a west-east pattern in the mid latitudes

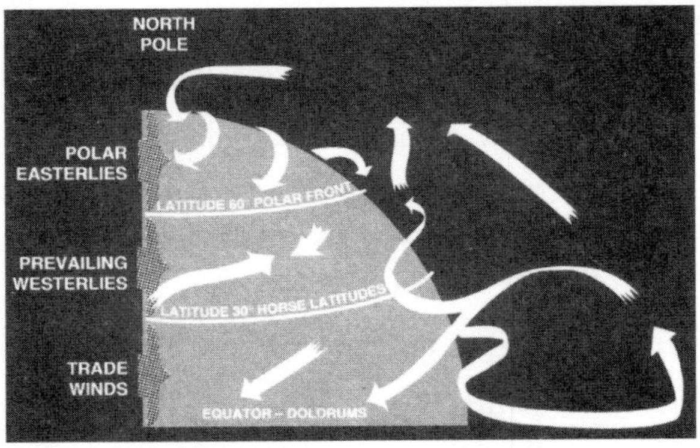

Figure 6-3. – Principle air currents in the Northern Hemisphere.

Pressure

- Heating and cooling of air causes it to change pressure
  - Hot air rises and expands, causing lower surface pressure
  - Cold air descends and contracts, causing higher surface pressure

Wind

- Wind is created as air moves from areas of high pressure to areas of low pressure
- Coriolis force causes air flowing into or out of a pressure system to rotate
  - Rotates clockwise around a high
  - Rotates counterclockwise around a low
- Air flows counterclockwise, up, and into a low
- Air flows clockwise, down, and out of a high

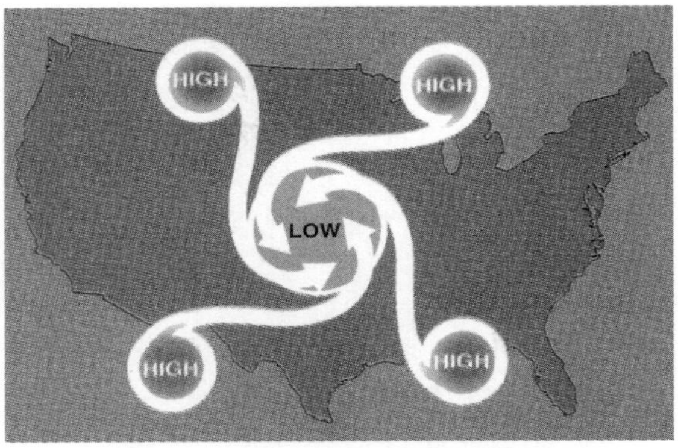

Figure 6-4. – Circulation of wind around a low.

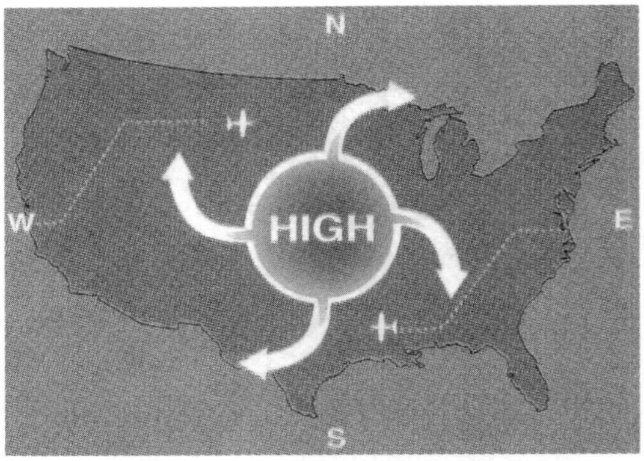

Figure 6-5. – Use of favorable winds in flight.

Moisture

- Earth's atmosphere contains 1% – 4% water vapor
  - This water vapor, interacting with the heat exchange, is responsible for all weather
- Moisture also retards the standard lapse rate
  - Moist-air lapse rate = 1° C per 1,000'
  - Standard lapse rate = 2° C per 1,000'
- Moisture influences "dew point"
  - Dew point = temperature to which air must be cooled to become saturated by water vapor already present in the air
  - Low temperature dew point spread = high humidity

Humidity

- Water vapor content of the air
- May be expressed as:
  - Relative humidity – The ratio of the existing amount of water vapor in the air at a given temperature to the maximum amount that could exist at that temperature; usually expressed as a percent
  - Mixing ratio – The ratio by weight of the amount of water vapor in a volume of air to the amount of dry air; usually expressed as grams / kilogram
  - Specific humidity – The ratio by weight of water vapor in a sample of air to the combined weight of water vapor and dry air

Stability

- Stability is the tendency of the atmosphere to resist upward movement
- Things which cause instability:
  - Heating from below – convective current (heat rises)
  - Low pressure – because of its lifting tendency
  - Cold air aloft – greater than normal lapse
    - When air rises, it cools at a rate of 2° C (5.4° F) per 1,000'
    - Greater differential between hot and cold air
  - Humidity – due to its slower lapse rate
- Characteristics of Stable Air
  - Smooth air
  - Poor visibility
  - Continuous precipitation (if any)
  - Stratus clouds
- Characteristics of Unstable Air
  - Turbulence
  - Good visibility
  - Showery precipitation (if any)
  - Cumulus clouds
- Temperature Inversions
  - A temperature inversion is an increase in temperature as altitude increases
  - Air beneath inversions is very stable
  - Low visibility
  - "Capping" effect on pollution
  - Develop near ground on cool, clear nights

Clouds

- Clouds are divided into four families, based on height
  - High – cirrus
  - Middle – alto
  - Low – (no prefix)
  - Extensive vertical development – towering cumulus (turbulent)

- Also grouped according to appearance
  - Cumulus = ragged or puffy; good indications of instability
  - Stratus = smooth and even; good indication of stability
- Combined description examples
  - Cirrostratus – high stratus
  - Altostratus – medium stratus
  - Stratus – low stratus
- Towering cumulus have extensive vertical development
  - Can quickly develop into thunderstorms
  - Visual indicator of heavy turbulence
- Rain Clouds
  - Rain clouds denoted by "nimbus"
  - Thunderstorms are called "cumulonimbus"
    - Cumulonimbus contain greatest turbulence
- When unsaturated air rises, it cools at a rate of 3° C (5.4° F) per 1,000'
  - Dew point decreases at 5/9° C (1° F) per 1,000'
  - Thus, temperature and dew point are converging at 2.5° C (4.4° F) per 1,000'
  - Use this formula to estimate base of convective clouds
  - If temperature = 15° C and dew point = 5° C, where are the bases?
    - 4000'
    - ((Temp - dew point) / 2.5) x 1000' or (Temp - dew point) x 400

Figure 6-6. – Cross-section of a cumulonimbus cloud

Air Masses

- Large areas of air that are formed over specific Earth regions
  - Polar Regions
  - Tropical regions
  - The oceans
- Air masses are constantly changing
  - Heating or cooling from below
  - Lifting or subsiding
  - Absorbing or losing moisture
- Its temperature is measured in relation to the temperature of the surface over which it is passing
  - A cold air mass has a colder temperature than the surface
    - Warmed from below, convection currents will be set up, causing turbulence
    - Improved visibility
    - Unstable
    - Types of clouds – cumulus and cumulonimbus
    - Ceilings – generally unlimited
    - Precipitation – occasional local thunderstorms or showers

- A warm air mass has a warmer temperature than the surface
  - No tendency for convection currents to form, resulting in smooth air
  - Poor visibility
  - Stable
  - Types of clouds – stratus and stratocumulus
  - Ceilings – generally low
  - Type of precipitation – drizzle
- Dissimilar air masses don't readily mix
  - They set up boundaries called frontal zones – fronts
    - The colder air mass projects under the warmer air mass
    - A warmer air mass rises over the colder air mass

Fronts

- There are four types of fronts
  - Warm front
  - Cold front
  - Occluded front
  - Stationary front
- Warm Front
  - The edge of an advancing warm air mass is called a warm front
    - Warmer air is overtaking and replacing the colder air
  - Cold air is more dense than warm air – the cold air hugs the ground
    - The warm air slides up and over the cold air
    - The cold air is slow to retreat in advance of the warm air
  - This slowness of air to retreat produces a more gradual frontal slope than the one in the cold front
    - Thus, a warm front, at the surface, is seldom as well marked as cold fronts
    - They move about half as fast

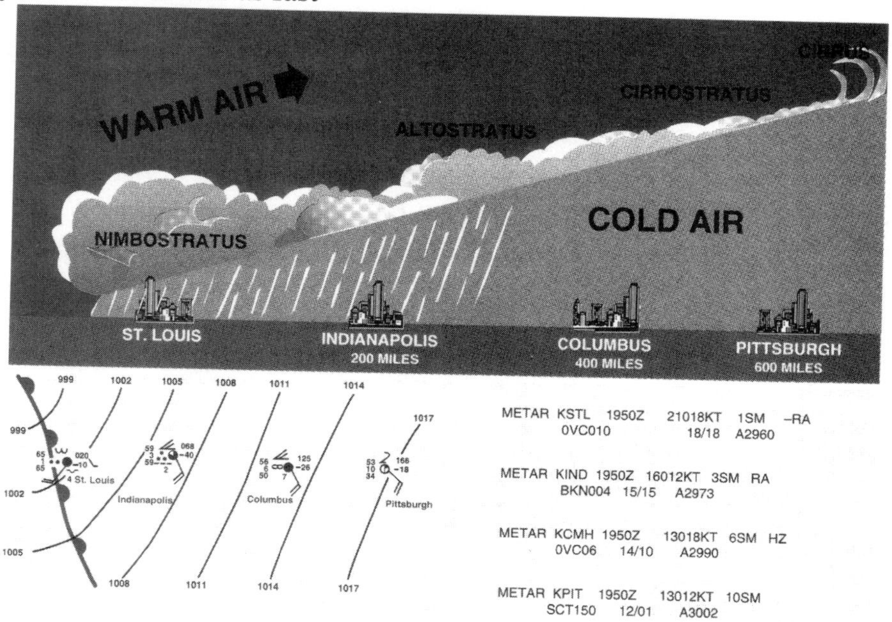

Figure 6-7. – Warm front: cross-section, as shown on weather map, as it appears on a METAR.

- Cold Front
  - The leading edge of an advancing cold air mass is called a cold front
  - The cold air is overtaking and replacing the warmer air
  - They move at about the speed of the wind component perpendicular to the front just above the frictional layer

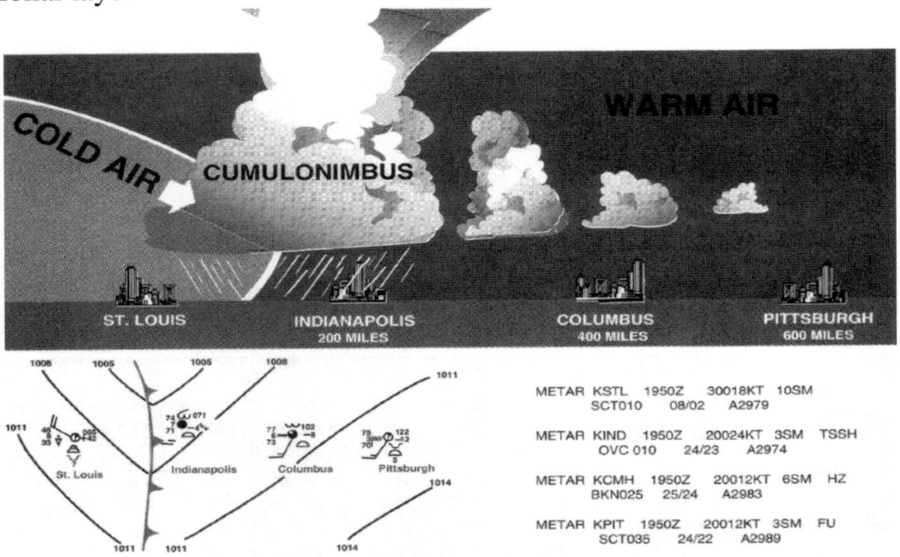

Figure 6-8. – Cold front: cross-section, as shown on weather map, and as reported on a METAR.

- Stationary Front
  - When neither air mass is replacing the other, the front is stationary
    - The opposing forces of the two air masses nullify one another and very little motion occurs
  - The surface winds tend to blow parallel to the frontal zone
  - The slope of the stationary front is shallow
- Occluded Front
  - When a cold front catches up with a warm front the two collide – where they collide is called an occluded front
    - The warm air, trapped between the two cold air masses, is forced aloft
  - The weather in an occlusion is a combination of both the warm front and the cold front
    - Warm – Lowered ceilings, lowered visibilities, precipitation
    - Cold – Squalls, turbulence, thunderstorms

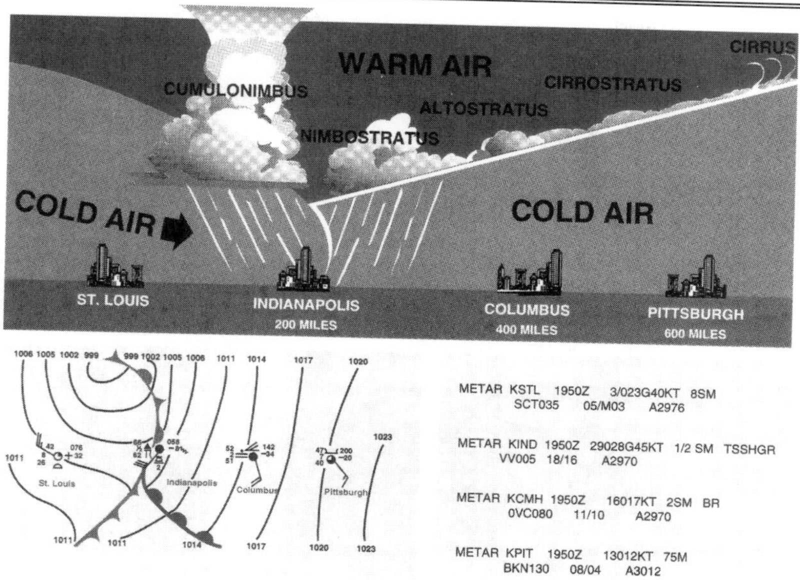

Figure 6-9. – Occluded front: cross-section, as shown on weather map, and as reported on a METAR.

Frontal Weather

- Warm Front weather (See Figure 6-7)
  - St. Louis weather: drizzle and fog
  - Indianapolis weather: overcast, nimbostratus, and continuous rain
  - Columbus weather: overcast, stratus and altocumulus, start of steady rain
  - Pittsburgh weather: high cirrus and cirrostratus
- Flying toward a warm front
  - 600 miles before the front – bright skies, unlimited visibility, and ceiling
  - 400 miles before the front – ceiling and visibility decrease rapidly
    - Rain begins shortly thereafter
  - 200 miles before the front – the ceilings would be low enough to stop VFR flight, and visibilities lowered to almost zero
  - As the front is approached, there is a gradual temperature increase and an increase in dew point, and atmospheric pressure would lessen
- Cold front weather (See Figure 6-8)
  - A narrow band of weather at the front
  - Scattered thunderstorms and showers
  - Could contain a continuous line of thunderstorms – squall line
    - Extremely turbulent air
  - Behind the front there is rapid clearing, gusty and turbulent wind, and cooler temperatures
- Flight toward a cold front
  - Beginning the flight in the warm air mass, sky likely overcast, stratocumulus clouds, smooth air and relatively low ceilings and visibilities until the flight was approaching the front
  - If the flight is continued into the frontal area, a few altostratus clouds and a dark layer of nimbostratus would likely be seen
    - Gusty wind and wind shifts
    - Possibility of squalls and cumulonimbus clouds
      - Too high to fly over, unsafe below them, and nearly impossible to fly through them

- Occluded front weather (See Figure 6-9)
  - The worst weather for the pilot
    - A combination of the warm front and cold front conditions
  - As it approaches, the warm front conditions are prevalent
    - Lowering ceilings, lowering visibilities, and precipitation
  - Followed almost immediately by cold front conditions
    - Squalls, turbulence, and thunderstorms

Thunderstorms

- The cumulonimbus cloud – thunderhead
  - Produce strong updrafts, large raindrops, hail, lightning, thunder, downdrafts, and strong turbulence
  - May exceed 50,000 feet in height
- Three Stages
  - Cumulus Stage
    - Updrafts and growth
  - Mature Stage
    - Up and downdrafts produce gusty surface winds
    - Precipitation begins
  - Dissipating Stage
    - Downdrafts
- Air mass thunderstorms
  - Often result from surface heating
  - Tend to self-destruct
  - 20-90 minute life-cycle
- Steady state thunderstorms
  - Associated with a weather system but may be intensified by afternoon heating
  - Tend to grow
  - Can last for hours
  - Physically, in its mature stage, the top of the cloud begins to flatten to an anvil shape and point in the direction the cloud is moving
    - There are strong updrafts at the leading edge of the cloud
    - Within the cloud and directly beneath it there are updrafts and downdrafts
    - The rear of the cloud generates strong downdrafts

Other Hazardous Weather Conditions

- Freezing rain is a real hazard to the pilot
  - Supercooled water droplets adhere rapidly on the surfaces of the aircraft and the windshield
  - Can obscure vision quickly
    - Do a 180 to where there was no freezing rain
- Icing – other than that caused by freezing rain – only occurs in the clouds
  - There is no reason for the VFR pilot to be in this situation
- Ground fog can form rapidly with the right conditions
  - It is especially dangerous at the time of takeoff and landing

- Fog can form
  - By cooling air to its dew point
    - Beware when the temperature / dew point spread is within 3 degrees of each other – as night approaches
  - Adding moisture to the air near the ground
- Frost on the wings of the aircraft can cause the aircraft to stall at a higher speed than normal
  - Frost can disrupt the smooth flow of air over the wing's surface
    - Don't fly with frost on the lifting surfaces of the aircraft
- Clear air turbulence implies turbulence which occurs outside of the clouds
  - Jet stream
  - Large thunderstorms – cumulonimbus clouds
  - Mountain waves

LESSON G7 – WEATHER REPORTS & FORECASTS

Note to Instructor

- Ensure that the student has current copies of each of these weather reports and forecasts available for this lesson
  - It may be beneficial to do this lesson in front of a computer so that obtaining these reports and forecasts can also be demonstrated
- Ensure that a current copy of AC 00-45 and the AIM are available for decoding reference
  - METAR decoding key Figure 7-17 and 7-1-8 in AIM
  - PIREP decoding key Figure 7-1-6 in AIM
  - TAF decoding key Figure 7-1-23 and 7-1-24 in AIM
  - See also, Pages 7-1-61 through 7-1-68 in AIM
- Emphasize the importance of learning to read and understand these reports!

Area Forecasts (FA)

- Forecasts of general weather conditions affecting a large area
- Issued three times daily
- Include two types of forecasts
  - 12-hour forecast
  - Additional 6-hour outlook
- Due to amount of data to be transmitted, area forecasts (FAs) use extensive abbreviations
  - Review
- Outlook Definitions:
  - VFR – Visibility > 5 SM & Cig > 3,000'
  - MVFR – Visibility 3-5 SM or Cig 1,000-3,000'
  - IFR – Visibility < 3 SM or Cig < 1,000'
- Review the current FA and decode it with the student

```
SLCC FA 141045
SYNOPSIS AND VFR CLDS/WX
SYNOPSIS VALID UNTIL 150500
CLDS/WX VALID UNTIL 142300...OTLK VALID
142300-150500
ID MT NV UT WY CO AZ NM

SEE AIRMET SIERRA FOR IFR CONDS AND MTN
OBSCN. TSTMS IMPLY PSBL SVR OR GTR TURBC
SVR ICG LLWS AND IFR CONDS.

NON MSL HGTS ARE DENOTED BY AGL OR CIG.

SYNOPSIS...HIGH PRES OVR NERN MT CONTG
EWD GRDLY. LOW PRES OVR AZ NM AND WRN
TX RMNG GENLY STNRY. ALF...TROF EXTDS
FROM WRN MT INTO SRN AZ RMNG STNRY.
```

Figure 7-1. – Partial example of an area forecast. (FA).

Surface Analysis Charts

- Representation of "big picture"
  - Graphically shows where highs, lows, & fronts are located
- Rules of thumb for surface analysis charts:
  - Highs usually (not always) bring good weather
  - Lows usually (not always) imply bad weather
  - Worst weather usually found near fronts
  - Fronts usually associated with Low Pressure
- Review the current Surface Analysis Chart with the student, focusing on the "big picture"

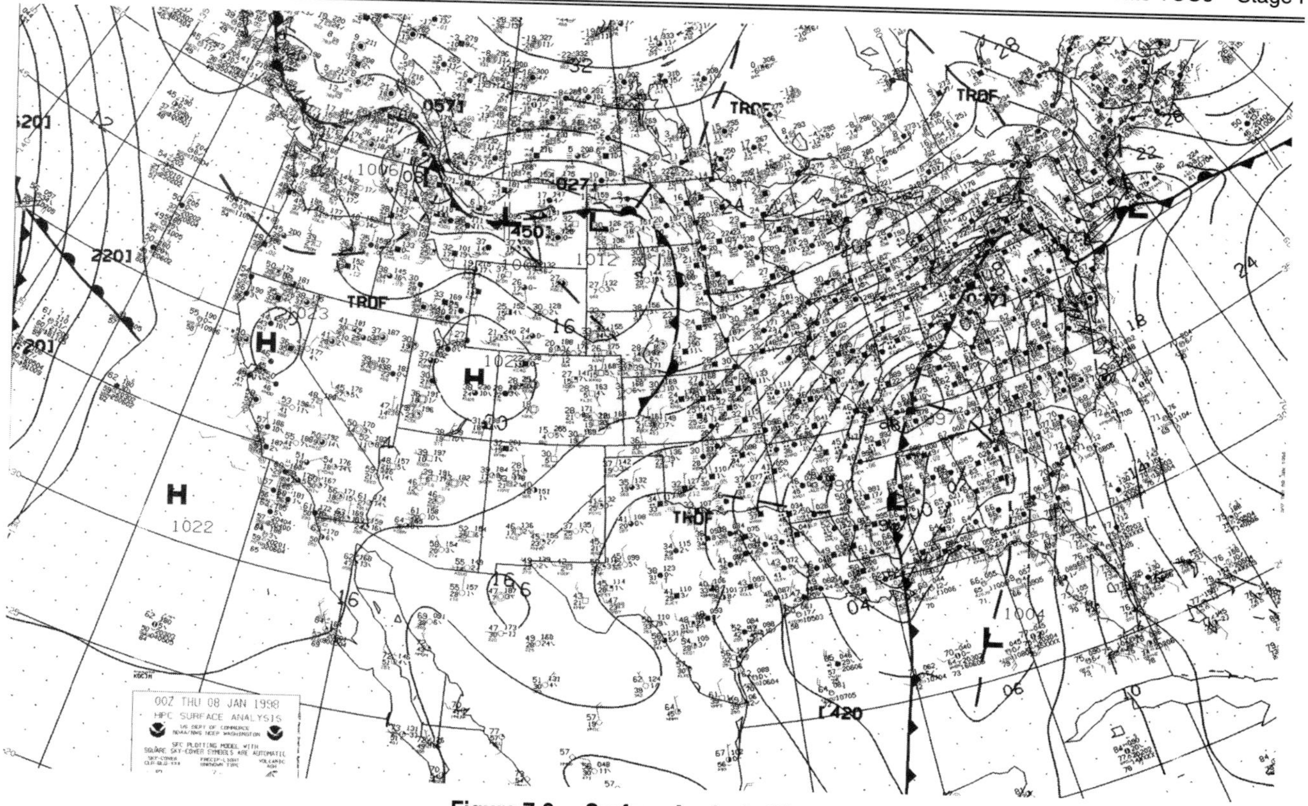

Figure 7-2. – Surface Analysis Chart.

TAFs

➢ Terminal Aerodrome Forecast

```
KPIR 111140Z 111212 13012KT P6SM BKN100 WS020/35035KT TEMPO 1214 5SM BR
     FM1500 16015G25KT P6SM SCT040 BKN250
     FM0000 14012KT P6SM BKN080 OVC150 PROB40 0004 3SM TSRA BKN030CB
     FM0400 14008KT P6SM SCT040 OVC080 TEMPO 0408 3SM TSRA OVC030CB
     BECMG 0810 32007KT=
```

Figure 7-3. – TAF.

➢ Weather Forecast for selected airports
- TAF – routine forecast
- TAF AMD – amended forecast

➢ Issued four times daily
- Issued at 0000, 0600, 1200, and 1800 (UTC)
- Valid for 24 hours
- There is some overlap between forecasts

➢ Review several of the current TAFs and decode them with the student

METARs

➢ Aviation Routine Weather Report
- Use abbreviations similar to TAFs

```
METAR KLAX 140651Z AUTO 00000KT 1SM R35L/4500V6000FT -RA BR BKN030 10/10
A2990 RMK A02
```

Figure 7-4. – METAR.

- Report of conditions at time of observation
  - METAR = regular hourly report
  - SPECI = special report necessitated by rapidly changing weather conditions
- Review several of the current METARs and decode them with the student

Winds and Temperatures Aloft (FD)

- Winds aloft are forecast for specific locations in the US

DATA BASED ON 010000Z
VALID 010600Z FOR USE 0500-0900Z. TEMPS NEG ABV 24000

FT	3000	6000	9000	12000	18000	24000	30000	34000	39000
MKC	2426	2726-09	2826-14	2930-21	2744-32	2751-41	275550	276050	731960
ABQ			1912+15	1914+07	1917-06	1820-17	172132	171942	192054

Figure 7-5. – Winds and Temperature Aloft.

- Four-digit group used to represent wind direction and speed
  - 2525 = 250° at 25 knots
  - 0315 = 030° at 15 knots
- Six-digit group is wind and temperature aloft
  - 353515 = 350° at 35 knots, temperature = 15° C
- Wind speed over 100 knots, forecaster adds 50 to direction and subtracts 100 from the speed
  - 7306-49 = 230° at 106 kts, temp = -49° C
- When wind speed is less than 5 knots, forecast is coded as 9900, which means light and variable
- Review several of the current FDs with the student

Pilot Reports

- Reports given to FSS by pilots in flight

```
UA /OV KMRB-KPIT/TM 1600/FL100/TP BE55/SK BKN024-TOP032/BKN-OVC043-TOPUNKN
/TA M12/IC LGT-MOD RIME 055-080
```

Figure 7-6. – Pilot Report.

- Can be a source of real-time, real life info
- Drawbacks:
  - Not everyone reports everything
  - In really bad weather, no one else has been a "trailblazer"
  - Age of report can be a factor
  - Applicability depends on aircraft type
- PIREPs are encouraged if unexpected weather is encountered
- Review several current PIREPs and decode them with the student

Obtaining a Weather Briefing FSS / DUAT

- Aviation weather reports given in Universal Coordinated Time (UTC) using 24 hour clock
  - Also referred to as "Zulu"
  - Obsolete term: "Greenwich Mean Time"
  - UTC is the time in Greenwich, England
  - A standard reference to eliminate time-zone confusion

TIME STANDARD TO UTC	
Eastern	+ 5 hr = UTC
Central	+ 6 hr = UTC
Mountain	+ 7 hr = UTC
Pacific	+ 8 hr = UTC
Alaskan	+ 9 hr = UTC
Hawaii	+ 10 hr = UTC
Subtract 1 hour for Daylight Time	

Figure 7-7. – Time Conversion

- Weather Briefings
  - Anywhere in US, call 1-800-WX-BRIEF
    - Routed to an Automated Flight Service Station (AFSS)
  - When calling, make sure briefer knows:
    - You are a pilot (or student pilot)
    - The intended route (or "local")
    - The departure / destination airports
    - Whether planning to fly VFR or IFR
    - Type of aircraft
    - Proposed departure time (UTC) and time en route
- Standard Briefings give info in this order:
  - Is there any bad weather happening?
  - What's the "big picture?"
    - Where are the highs, lows and fronts?
  - What are the current conditions?
  - What's forecast for the near future?
  - Any needed data re: airport closures, etc.
- Other Weather Sources
  - Self-briefing sources
    - DUATS – Direct User Access Terminal Service
      - www.duats.com or www.duat.com or direct dial via modem
      - Free service supported by FAA
      - Official weather briefings via computer
      - Account available to anyone with valid medical or pilot certificate
    - Computer Briefing Services
      - DTN, WSI, etc.
    - Web-based briefings
      - http://aviationweather.gov – Aviation Weather Center in Kansas City, MO
      - www.weather.com – good for general (non-aviation) weather info
    - CAUTION: Computer based sources, other than DUATS, may not be acceptable as an FAA "official" briefing! Check the provider's latest credentials

Standard / Abbreviated / Outlook Briefings

- Get a "Standard Briefing" before each flight
- "Outlook Briefing" forecasts for flights more than 6 hours out
- "Abbreviated Briefing" is used to
  - Supplement available data
  - Update a previous briefing
  - Find out some specific information

LESSON G8 – WEATHER REPORTS & FORECASTS

Note to Instructor

- ➢ Ensure that the student has current copies of each of these weather reports and forecasts available for this lesson
  - It may be beneficial to do this lesson in front of a computer so that obtaining these reports and forecasts can also be demonstrated
- ➢ Ensure that a current copy of AC 00-45 and the AIM are available for decoding reference
- ➢ Emphasize the importance of learning to read and understand these reports!

Radar Wx Reports

- ➢ Radar Weather Report (SD)
  - Text report regarding areas of precipitation appearing on radar
  - Indicates the type, intensity, location, movement, and height of the echo top
    - ▪ All heights are reported above sea level
  - Also referred to as RAREPs
- ➢ Radar Summary Charts
  - Charts displaying collection of radar reports
  - Shows tops of clouds, direction of movement
  - Intensity indicated by contours
    - ▪ Report combines 6 levels to produce 3 contours
    - ▪ Levels formerly called video integrator processor (VIP) levels

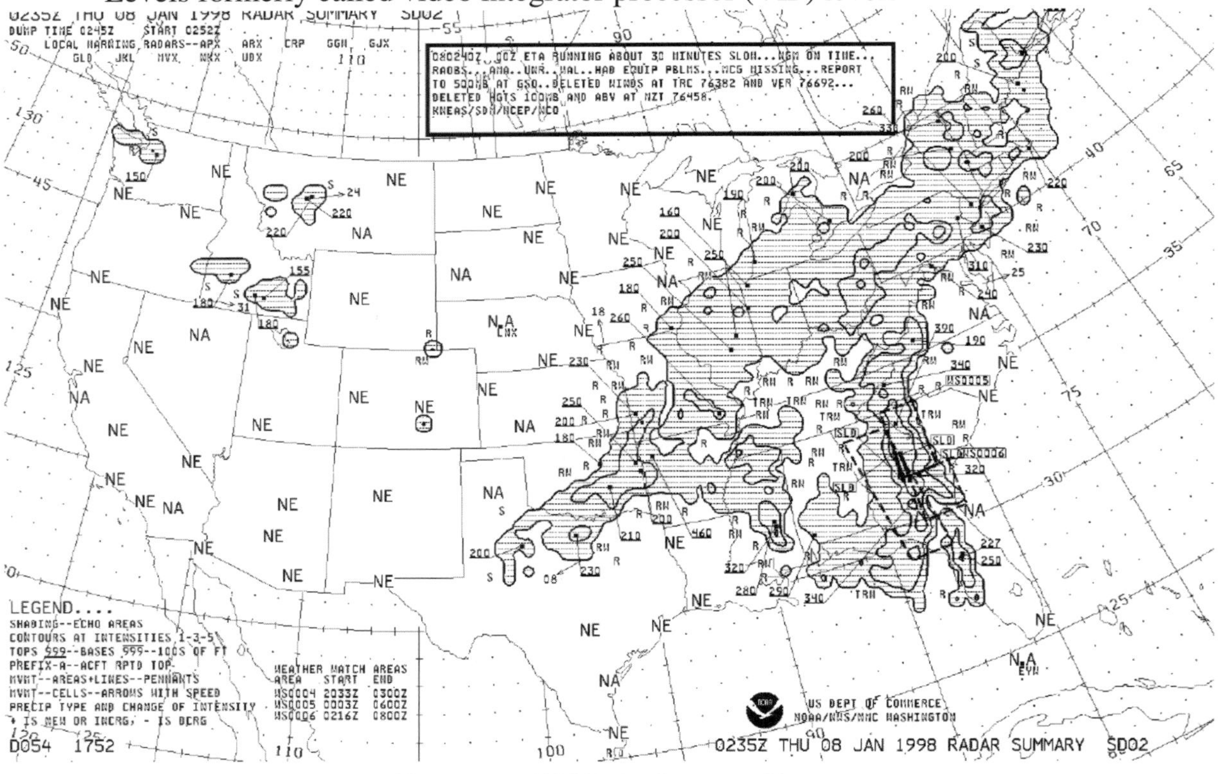

Figure 8-1. – NWS Radar Summary Chart.

Severe Wx Reports and Forecasts

- Convective Outlook (AC)
  - National forecast of thunderstorms
  - Flight planning tool used to avoid thunderstorms
  - Three forecasts:
    - Day 1 Convective Outlook (first 24 hours) issued at 0600Z, 1300Z, 1630Z, 2000Z, and 0100Z
    - Day 2 Convective Outlook (next 24 hours) issued at 0830Z (ST) / 0730Z (DT) and updated at 1730Z
    - Day 3 Convective Outlook (next 24 hours) issued from day 3 at 1200Z to day 4 at 1200Z
  - Define areas at risk for severe and general (non-severe) thunderstorms
    - Severe thunderstorm criteria:
      - Winds equal to or greater than 50 knots at the surface
      - Hail equal to or greater than ¾ inch in diameter at the surface
      - Tornadoes
  - Also plotted on Convective Outlook Chart

```
MKC AC 291435
CONVECTIVE OUTLOOK... REF AFOS NMCGPH94O.
VALID 291500Z-301200Z

THERE IS A SLGT RISK OF SVR TSTMS TO THE RIGHT OF A LINE FROM 10 NE JAX 35 NNW AYS
AGS 15 E SPA 30 NE CLT 25 N FAY 30 ESE EWN.

GEN TSTMS ARE FCST TO THE RIGHT OF A LINE FROM 55 ESE YUM 30 NE IGM 15 S CDC 30 SW
U24 25 ESE ELY 40 W P38 DRA 50 SW DRA 50 NW NID SAC 30 E ACV 25 E ONP 40 E BLI.

...SEVERE THUNDERSTORM FORECAST DISCUSSION...
 .SERN U.S...

COOL FRONT CONTS SC/NC BORDER. VERY MOIST AND UNSTBL AMS ALONG AND S OF FRONT
E OF APLCHNS WITH CAPES TO REACH TO 4000 J/KG WITH AFTN HEATING. ALTHOUGH WIND
PROFILES ARE WK...COMB OF FRONTAL CNVGNC COUPLED WITH SEA BREEZE FRONT WILL
INITIATE PULSE SVR TSTMS VCNTY AND S OF FRONT THIS AFTN/EVE. PRIMARY SVR EVENTS
WILL BE WET DOWNBURST TO PUSH SWD FROM CNTRL RCKYS EWD TO MID ATLC CST. E OF
APLCNS FRONT NOW LCTD VCNTY WND DMG.

...GENERAL THUNDERSTORM FORECAST DISCUSSION
...GULF CST AREA INTO SRN PLNS...

SFC FNT CURRENTLY LOCATED FM THE CAROLINAS WWD INTO PARTS OF OK WL CONT TO
SAG SLOWLY SWD ACRS THE SRN APLCNS/LWR MS VLY THRU THE REMAINDER OF THE PD. S
OF THE BNDRY...A VRY MOIST AMS RMNS IN PLACE AS DWPNTS ARE IN THE MID TO UPR 70S.
WHILE SOME CLDNS IS PRESENT ACRS THE AREA...SUF HEATING SHOULD OCR TO ALLOW
FOR MDT TO STG AMS DSTBLZN DURG THE LATE MRNG/ERY AFTN. AS A RESULT...SFC BASED
CAPE VALUES SHOULD BE AOA 2000 J/KG THIS AFTN. BNDRYS FM OVERNIGHT CNVTN AS WELL
AS SEA BREEZE CIRCULATIONS SHOULD BE SUF TO INITIATE SCT TO NMRS TSTMS ACRS THE
AREA. MID TO UPR LVL FLOW IS RELATIVELY WK...SO THIS SUG ORGANIZED SVR TSTM ACTVTY
IS NOT LIKELY.
```

Figure 8-2. – Sample Convective Outlook (AC).

- Severe Weather Watch Bulletin (WW)
  - Define areas of possible severe thunderstorms or tornado activity
    - A severe thunderstorm watch describes areas of expected severe thunderstorms
    - A tornado watch describes areas where the threat of tornadoes exists
  - Unscheduled and issued as required
  - Preliminary notification of a watch called the Alert Severe Weather Watch bulletin (AWW) is sent before the WW to alert necessary personnel
- Hurricane Advisory (WH)
  - Advisory issued when hurricane threatens a coastline, but is located at least 300 nm offshore
  - Issued to alert aviation interests
  - Gives the location of the storm center, its expected movement, and the maximum winds in and near the storm center
  - Does not contain details of associated weather
- Center Weather Advisory (CWA)
  - Aviation warning for use by air crews to anticipate and avoid adverse weather conditions in the en route and terminal environments
  - Not a flight planning product
    - Reflects current conditions expected at the time of issuance and/or is a short-range forecast for conditions expected to begin within 2 hours of issuance
  - Valid for a maximum of 2 hours
    - If conditions are expected to continue beyond the 2-hour valid period, a statement will be included in the CWA

AIRMETs

- Airmen's Meteorological Information
- Issued to warn of weather hazards to small aircraft
  - Moderate icing (AIRMET Zulu)
  - Moderate turbulence (AIRMET Tango)
  - IFR conditions (AIRMET Sierra)
  - Sustained surface winds of more than 30 kts
  - Extensive mountain obscuration (Sierra)

```
CHIS WA 121345
AIRMET SIERRA UPDT 3 FOR IFR AND MTN OBSCN VALID UNTIL 122000.
AIRMET IFR...SD NE MN IA MO WI LM MI IL IN KY
FROM 70NW RAP TO 50W RWF TO 50W MSN TO GRB TO MBS TO FWA TO CVG TO HNN TO TRI TO
ARG TO 40SSW BRL TO OMA TO BFF TO 70NW RAP
OCNL CIG BLW 010/VIS BLW 3SM FG/BR. CONDS ENDG 15Z-17Z. .

AIRMET MTN OBSCN...KY TN
FROM HNN TO TRI TO CHA TO LOZ TO HNN
MTNS OCNL OBSC CLDS/PCPN/BR. CONDS ENDG TN PTN AREA 18Z- 20Z.CONTG KY BYD
20Z..ENDG 02Z.
```

Figure 8-3. – Sample AIRMET.

SIGMETs / Convective SIGMETs

- Significant Meteorological Information
- Issued for weather hazards to ALL aircraft
  - Severe turbulence
  - Severe icing
  - Dust storms, sand storms, or volcanic ash
  - Volcanic eruption

```
BOSR WS 050600
SIGMET ROMEO 2 VALID UNTIL 051000
ME NH VT
FROM CAR TO YSJ TO CON TO MPV TO CAR
MOD TO OCNL SEV TURB BLW 080 EXP DUE TO STG NWLY FLOW. CONDS CONTG BYD 1000Z.
```

Figure 8-4. – Example of a SIGMET.

- Convective SIGMETs (WST)
  - Special type of SIGMET
  - Severe thunderstorm activity
    - Tornadoes
    - Lines of thunderstorms
    - Severe turbulence
    - Severe icing
    - Embedded thunderstorms
- If possible, get an AIRMET / SIGMET map to go along with text descriptions
  - AIRMET / SIGMET areas are described in a "dot-to-dot" fashion, using airport IDs as the points

NOTAMs

- Notices to Airmen
- Method of transmitting important information to all pilots
  - Airport or runway closures
  - Maintenance of navigation beacons
  - Radio tower light outages
  - Any other safety issues which pilots need to know about
- Types of NOTAMs
  - NOTAM (L) – local NOTAMs
    - Affect local airport users
      - Grass cutting operations
      - Taxiways closed
  - NOTAM (D) – distant NOTAMs
    - Affect mainly cross-country pilots
      - Closed airports
      - Navigation aids off the air

- NOTAM (FDC) – Flight Data Center
  - Changes in regulations or charts
  - Emergency flight restrictions
    - National airspace closure information (due to September 11, 2001 terrorist attacks) was conveyed via FDC NOTAM system
  - Wide-spread traffic delays or closures

➢ NOTAM information should be contained in Standard FSS briefing

Wind Shear Reports

➢ Wind shear is a change in wind speed and/or wind direction in a short distance resulting in a tearing or shearing effect

➢ Report the loss or gain of airspeed and the altitudes at which it was encountered

➢ Pilots should promptly volunteer reports to controllers of wind shear conditions encountered

➢ A controller may issue a wind shear alert based upon information derived from equipment in the control tower

Wind Shear Recognition and Avoidance

➢ Wind shear can exist in a horizontal or vertical direction and occasionally in both

➢ Shows up as a momentary change in airspeed or altitude (or rate of altitude change)
- Can be VERY DANGEROUS at low altitudes!

➢ Avoidance
- Key to avoidance is recognizing the problem then going elsewhere if possible
- Understand conditions conducive to development
  - Convective storms (thunderstorms, rain / snow showers)
  - Fronts
  - Strong surface winds
  - Unstable (turbulent) air
  - Strong winds on top of temperature inversion
- Listen for reports from other pilots (or ATC)
- Watch for conflicting wind indications

Weather Related Aeronautical Decision Making & Judgment

➢ The best place to make a weather related aeronautical decision is on the ground

➢ Responsibility
- Early – Instructor
- Later – Student

➢ Develop alternative plans for non-forecasted weather before a decision becomes critical

➢ Don't delay utilizing the alternative plans

➢ When in doubt, err on the conservative side

➢ Encourage the student to develop a personal minimums checklist related to weather and stay within its guidelines

LESSON G9 – AIRCRAFT SYSTEMS

Note to Instructor

- Ensure that the student has an AFM/POH for the training aircraft available for this discussion
- Utilize the diagrams as required
- Emphasize the importance of knowing these systems very well
- If practical, pointing out the systems on an aircraft undergoing maintenance (cowling off or inspection ports open) can be helpful

Fuel System

- Two major types of fuel delivery systems on reciprocating engines
  - Carbureted systems
  - Fuel injected systems
- Float-Type Carbureted Fuel Systems
  - Filtered air drawn into carburetor
  - Drawn into a narrow "throat" or venturi
    - Low pressure area is created in venturi
    - Low pressure area draws fuel into airstream
  - Air and fuel mix are then drawn into engine
  - Carburetors are very simple and reliable

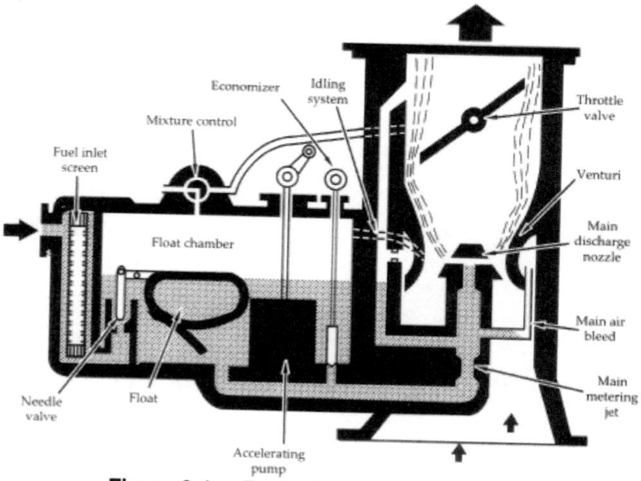

Figure 9-1. – Basic float type carburetor.

- Pressure-type carburetors operate on a similar principle to float-type but won't be discussed here
- Fuel / Air Mixture
  - At higher altitudes, fuel / air mixture must be leaned to decrease fuel flow in thinner air
    - Descending without enriching mixture, mixture will be too lean
  - At high altitude airports (above 3,000'), lean the mixture to give best RPM at full power
- Fuel Injection Systems
  - Air enters through the intake manifold
  - Fuel is squirted directly into the cylinder or just prior to the cylinder's intake valve
  - Injectors are more efficient than carburetors
    - Not prone to icing
  - Vapor lock / hot starts a problem
- Review training aircraft's fuel system with student
- Fuel Types
  - Jet fuel
    - Kerosene based
    - Clear
    - Heavy, oily fuel
  - Aviation gasoline
    - 100LL = Blue
    - 100 Octane = Green
    - 80 Octane = Red

- Fuel Sampling
  - Drain a fuel sample before every flight
  - Check for contamination
    - Don't fly with colorless fuel in a recip!
      - It could mean mixed octanes
      - It could be jet fuel
      - It could be water
        - Water and fuel don't mix
        - Water settles to bottom in a bubble-like globule
  - Use next higher octane grade if the proper grade for the aircraft is not available

- Other Fuel System Considerations
  - Vents must be free of obstructions!
  - Electrically ground the airplane before fueling
    - Prevent static electricity buildup
    - Spark could cause fire
  - Filling tanks at the end of the day prevents condensation by eliminating air space in tanks
  - Electric pumps are provided in case engine-driven pumps fail

Electrical System

- Electrical system runs radios, lights, etc.

- Doesn't run engine (ignition is separate)

- Electrical system power components
  - Battery
    - Provides power for starting
    - Runs radios, lights, etc.
  - Alternator / generator
    - Recharges battery

- Review the electrical system schematic for the training aircraft with the student

- Master Switch
  - Switch controls electrical system
  - Often a two-part switch
    - Can isolate alternator from system, but leave battery on-line
    - In case of a defective alternator, this allows the aircraft's electrical system to be run off the battery only

Environmental System

- Ventilation provided by air flow being directed inside the cabin

- Heat provided by airflow within a shroud over the outside of the exhaust system or a separate heater
  - Since most aircraft engines are air-cooled, there is no hot water to circulate into cockpit

Primary Flight Controls and Trim Systems

- Additional information on primary flight controls, trim, and flaps may be found in *Lesson G3*
- The flight control system is comprised of cockpit controls, cables, pulleys and linkages connected to the movable control surfaces outside the aircraft
- Three primary flight control systems:
  - Elevator
  - Aileron
  - Rudder
- Two secondary flight control systems:
  - Trim tabs
    - Allow the pilot to eliminate control pressures
  - Wing flaps
    - Allow the pilot to change the lifting characteristics of the wing and also to change the speed at which the wing stalls

Leading Edge Devices and Spoilers

- Slots at the front of the wing may be used to energize the airflow over the wing at high angles of attack, delaying the stall separation
  - Fixed slots increase drag in cruise flight attitudes
- Slats are devices that move to create leading edge slots at low speeds and high angles of attack and close during cruise flight to reduce drag
  - May be activated manually or by the shifting pressures at various angles of attack
- Leading edge flaps are aerodynamic control surfaces on the front of the wing that increase the lift produced by the wing by increasing the curvature of the airfoil
  - Leading edge flaps are used to increase lift at low airspeeds
- Stall strips are long, narrow, triangular-shaped wedges attached to some aircraft's leading edges
  - The purpose of a stall strip is to "force" an aerodynamic stall close to the root area first
    - The strips cause separation of airflow over the wing to occur at a lower angle of attack than if the strips were not in place
- Spoilers are flap like deflectors that can be raised into the air flowing over an airfoil
  - When raised into the airstream, the spoiler disturbs the smooth flow of air and destroys part of the lift

Wing Flap System

- Training aircraft use three main types of flap actuators:
  - Electrical
  - Mechanical
  - Hydraulic
- Types of flaps
  - Plain
  - Split
  - Fowler
  - Slotted

LESSON G10 – AIRCRAFT SYSTEMS

Powerplant

- Different types of aircraft powerplants (engines)
  - Turbine – pure jet and turbo fan engines
  - Turboprop – jet engine driving a propeller through a gearbox system
  - Reciprocating – internal combustion engines, similar to a car engine, driving a propeller
    - Back and forth motion of one or more pistons is converted to a rotational motion via a crankshaft
- Parts of a Reciprocating Engine
  - Crankcase
  - Cylinders
  - Pistons
  - Wrist pins
  - Connecting rods
  - Intake valves
  - Exhaust valves
  - Rocker arms
  - Push rods
  - Crankshaft
  - Camshaft
  - Spark plugs
  - Magnetos (Ignition)

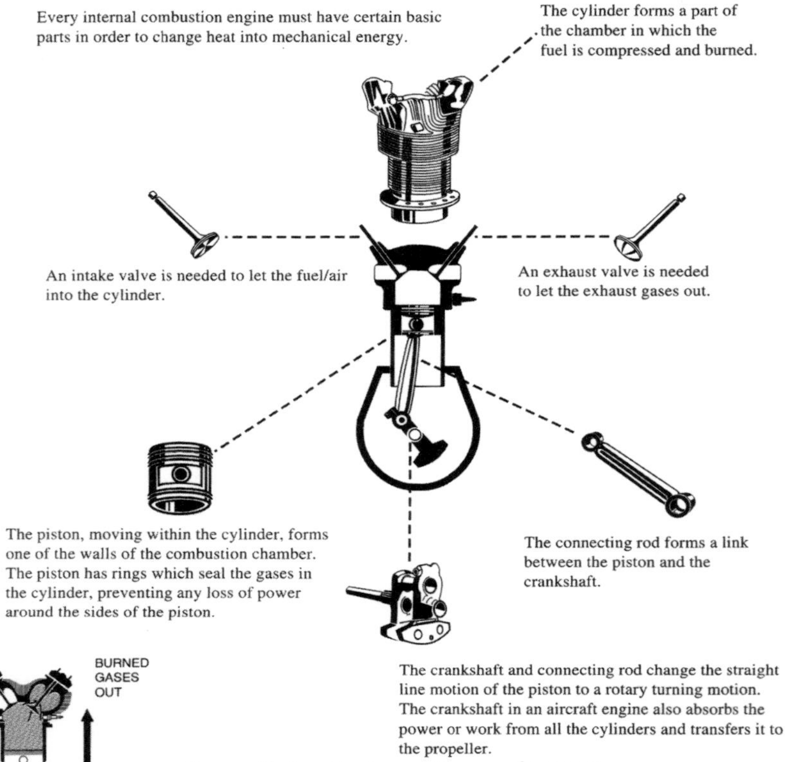

Figure 10-1. – Reciprocating engine parts.

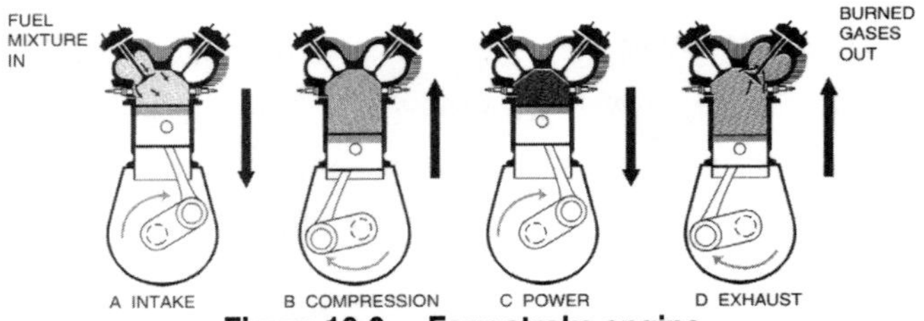

Figure 10-2. – Four stroke engine.

- 4-Stroke – 5-Event per Cycle
  - Intake stroke / event
  - Compression stroke / event
  - Ignition event
  - Power stroke / event
  - Exhaust stroke / event
- Basic Types of Recips
  - In-Line
    - Upright or inverted
  - V-Type
    - Upright or inverted
  - Opposed
    - Horizontal or vertical
  - Radial
    - Single or Multi row

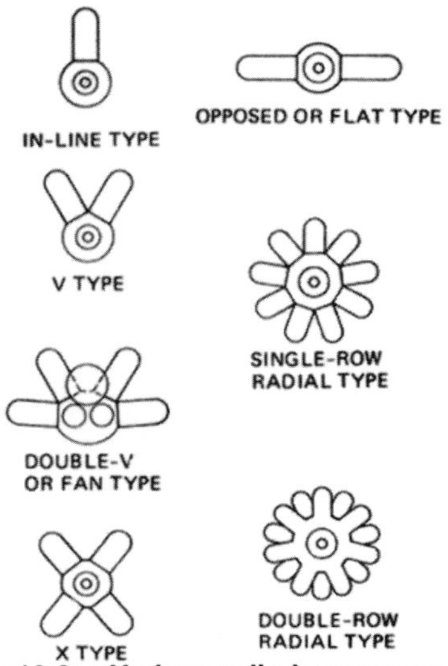

Figure 10-3. – Various cylinder arrangements.

- Engine Cooling
  - Combustion in cylinders produces heat
    - Heat must be removed to avoid damaging engine
    - Types of cooling:
      - Water cooled
      - Air cooled
        - Most common type of aircraft cooling
        - Simple, safe, light-weight
  - Air-Cooled Engines
    - Engine cooling occurs two ways
      - Air flowing over the cylinder cooling fins
      - Oil circulating through the engine
        - Provides a type of "liquid cooling"
        - Lubrication
        - Oil circulation is responsible for majority of engine cooling
  - Engine overheating caused by
    - Operating with too much power
      - Especially on the ground
    - Climbing too steeply in hot weather
    - Using fuel with lower octane than specified
    - Operating with mixture too lean
    - Low oil level
  - Effects of high heat
    - Can warp metal parts in the engine
    - Parts are "bent out of shape" and cause...
      - Loss of power
      - Excessive oil consumption
      - Excessive internal wear
  - Reduce overheating by reversing the causal conditions
    - Reduce power
    - Reduce the climb angle
    - Use fuel with correct octane
    - Enrich the mixture
    - Make sure oil level and pressure are sufficient
- Combustion Problems – Detonation
  - Occurs when fuel / air mixture explodes violently instead of rapidly burning smoothly
  - Generally caused by lower-than recommended octane or too lean a mixture
  - Causes engine damage
  - Causes higher operating temperatures

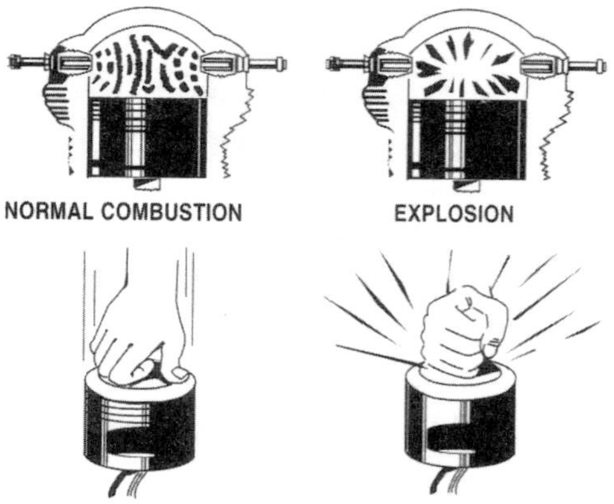

Figure 10-4. – Normal combustion and explosive combustion.

- Combustion Problems – Pre-Ignition
  - Fuel / air charge burns early and in an uncontrolled fashion
  - Caused by hot spots on the cylinder walls or piston head
    - Hot spots may be due to previous detonation damage
  - Causes pronounced loss of power

- Preventing Combustion Problems
  - Keep the temperature under control
    - Enrich mixture
    - Reduce power
    - Lower the nose and increase speed
  - Use the correct fuel!

Propeller

- Rotating airfoil

- Blade is twisted
  - Angle changes from the hub to the tip to produce uniform lift

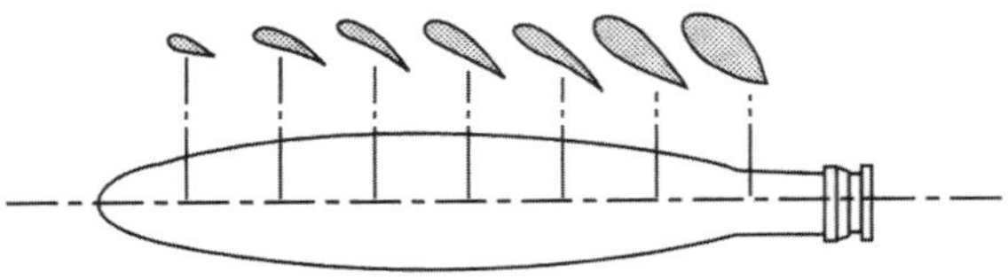

Figure 10-5. – Changes in propeller blade angle from hub to tip.

- Currently two major types
  - Fixed-pitch
    - Has only a throttle control
  - Controllable-pitch
    - May be a simple two position system or a more complex constant-speed system
    - Typically has both a throttle and a propeller control

Hydraulic System

- Types of Hydraulic Brake Systems
  - Independent
    - Generally used on small aircraft
    - Independent of any other hydraulic system
    - Consists of:
      - Reservoir
      - 1-2 Master cylinder(s)
      - Mechanical linkage from each pedal to its master cylinder
      - Connecting fluid lines
      - Brake assembly on each main landing gear wheel
  - Power control
    - Used on large aircraft requiring a large volume of brake fluid to activate the brakes
  - Power boost
    - Used on fast but smaller aircraft
  - Other types of hydraulic systems
    - Gear
    - Flaps

Ignition System

- System which provides a spark, at the correct moment, for the fuel / air mixture
- Aircraft use dual ignition systems
  - Two sparkplugs per cylinder improves performance
  - Increases safety by providing redundancy
  - Each plug is fired by a different magneto or ignition circuit

Carburetor Heat / Air Induction System

- Carburetor Icing Problems
  - Vaporizing fuel lowers temperature of air
  - Moisture in the air can freeze in venturi
  - Carb icing likely when…
    - Using low throttle settings
    - Operating in extremely humid conditions
  - Visible moisture and low air temperatures are not required for carb icing
- Carbureted aircraft have air preheaters which prevents / melts carb ice
  - Use carb heat as recommended by manufacturer

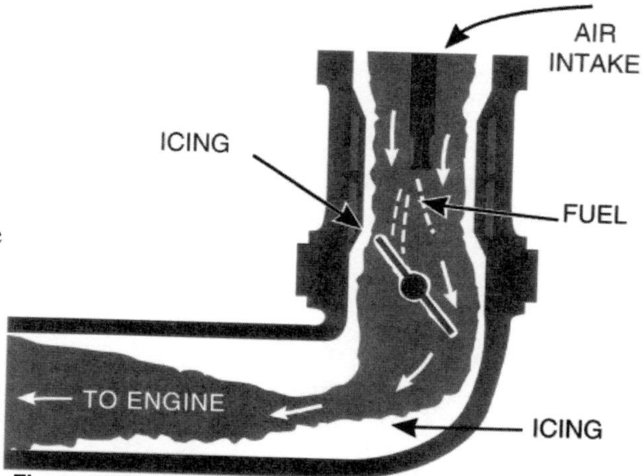

Figure 10-6. – Formation of ice in the carburetor reduces or even blocks the flow of air and fuel to the engine.

- Carb heat cautions
  - Carb heat makes air hotter and less dense
  - Enriches the mixture, affects performance
  - Don't operate for extended periods of time with carb heat on
  - Make sure carb heat is off for takeoffs and go-arounds
- Fuel injected engines are not prone to icing in the air and fuel delivery system though the primary air induction system may become blocked in icing conditions
  - An alternate air source is incorporated in the cowling
    - Typically operates automatically with a manual backup
    - May also heat the air

Aircraft Equipment List

- Aircraft equipment list is more restrictive than 91.205
- It specifies required equipment for a specific airplane based upon its certification
- Also specifies optional equipment, standard, etc.
- Generally provides station arms required for weight and balance calculations

VFR Required Equipment

- 14 CFR Section 91.205 specifies required equipment for day VFR operations
- A TOMATO FLAMES
  - A – Anti-collision lights (if certified after 1996)
  - T – Tachometer for each engine
  - O – Oil pressure gauge for each engine
  - M – Magnetic compass
  - A – Airspeed Indicator
  - T – Temperature gauge for liquid cooled engines
  - O – Oil temperature gauge for air-cooled engines
  - F – Fuel Gauge
  - L – Landing gear indicator (if applicable)
  - A – Altimeter
  - M – Manifold pressure gauge for altitude engines
  - E – ELT
  - S – Shoulder belt / lap belt for each occupant

Inoperative Equipment

- If there is an approved Minimum Equipment List (MEL) for a specific aircraft, it must be followed
- If no MEL, the small airplane pilot may elect to continue operations under certain conditions
  - The inoperative instruments and equipment must not:
    - Be required by airworthiness regulations
    - Be indicated as required on the aircraft's equipment list
    - Be required by 14 CFR Section 91.205 or other rules
    - Be required to be operational by an airworthiness directive
    - Constitute a hazard to the aircraft as determined by a pilot or mechanic
  - The inoperative equipment must be handled in one of the following ways:
    - Removed, the cockpit control placarded, and the maintenance recorded
    - Deactivated and placarded "Inoperative"
    - For the anti-collision light system, may continue to a repair location
- Special Flight Permits
  - Special flight (ferry) permit may be issued to:
    - Fly an aircraft to a repair or storage facility
    - Deliver or export an aircraft
    - Flight test new production aircraft
    - Evacuate aircraft from area of impending danger
    - Conduct customer demonstration flights in new production aircraft
    - Allow operations over the maximum gross weight for an over water flight
  - Pilot must submit the following to the FAA:
    - The purpose of the flight
    - The proposed itinerary
    - The crew required
    - The ways the aircraft is non-compliant with regs
    - Restrictions required for safety
    - Other information requested

Landing Gear

- Landing gear must be capable of:
  - Steering
    - A steerable or castering nose gear or tailwheel
  - Braking
    - Individual brakes are installed on each main gear
      - Can be applied together or separately
  - Absorbing shock
    - Hydraulic shock struts or leaf springs help absorb the impact of landing
- Two basic types of landing gear:
  - Conventional
    - Comprised of two main gear and a tailwheel
  - Tricycle
    - Comprised of two main gear and a steerable nose wheel
      - Provides better ground handling characteristics
- Some aircraft have retractable landing gear
  - Reduces drag
  - Increases airspeed
  - Increases cost and complexity
  - Accomplished electrically or hydraulically
    - Cockpit indicators provide information on the status of the gear

Oil System

- Lubricating oil serves two purposes:
  - It coats the surfaces of the moving parts to:
    - Reduce friction
    - Dissipate heat build up
  - It absorbs and dissipates much of the heat generated by the engine
- Engine oil is stored in a sump at the bottom of the engine crankcase
  - A pump forces oil from the sump to the various parts of the engine
- The engine has an oil pressure gauge to monitor its workings
  - The oil pressure gauge indicates specific pressure and has an arc to indicate normal operating range with marks to indicate high and low oil pressure
- Loss of oil pressure is usually followed by engine failure
- There is an oil temperature gauge as well
  - It is calibrated in Celsius or Fahrenheit and is color coded
- Check the oil level before each flight
- Follow the manufacturer's recommendation for the proper grade of oil to use

LESSON G11 – AIRCRAFT SYSTEMS

Vacuum System

- Vacuum or pressure system may be used to power gyroscopic instruments
  - Also, other systems on advanced aircraft
- Draws a stream of air over rotor vanes to spin the gyro inside the instrument
  - Engine driven vacuum pump
  - Regulator
  - Air filter
  - Gauge
  - Manifold and tubing

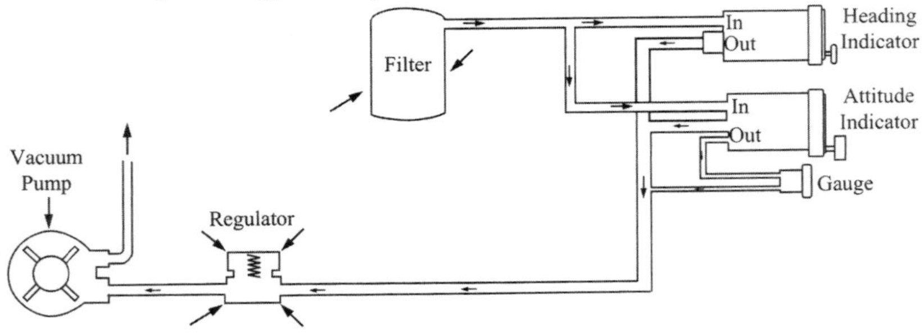

Figure 11-1. – Typical pump-driven vacuum system.

Gyroscopic Instruments

- What is a gyroscope?
  - Rotating body of mass
  - Principles are based on Newton's Laws
    - A body at rest will remain at rest..... unless acted upon by an outside force
    - F=M x A
    - For every force there is an equal & opposite force
      - Not the most important here
- Gyroscopic Inertia
  - Weight
  - Angular velocity (speed)
  - Radius for the location of mass
  - Bearing friction

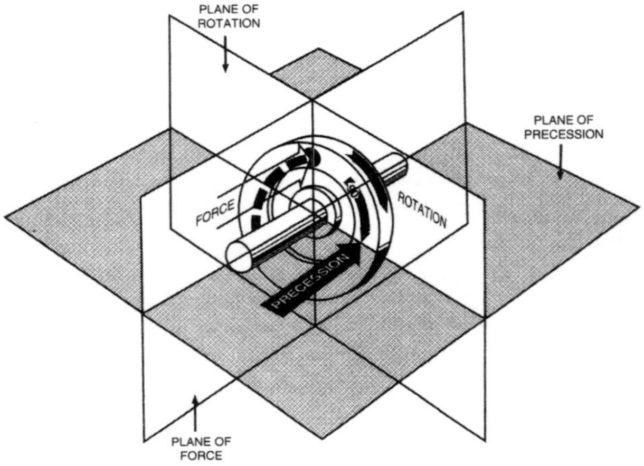

Figure 11-2. – Gyroscopic precession.

- Principles of a Gyroscope
  - Rigidity in space
  - Precession
- Attitude Indicator
  - Also called artificial horizon
  - Shows movement around the lateral & longitudinal axis
    - Pitch & roll
  - Gyro mounted on double gimble
  - Erecting mechanism
    - Used at start
    - Corrects precession errors
  - Slight error may be apparent after 180 degrees of turn

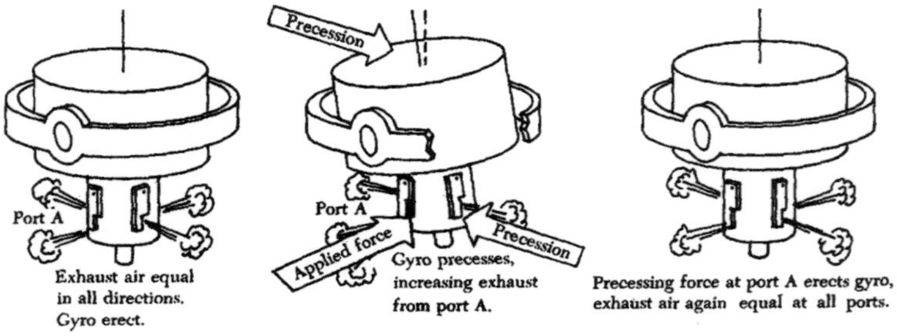

Figure 11-3. – Erecting mechanism using pendulous vanes.

- Heading Indicator
  - Also called the directional gyro
  - Used to overcome the errors associated with the magnetic compass
  - Vertically mounted gyro
  - Errors due to precession
    - Reset to magnetic heading

Figure 11-4. – Heading indicator.

- Turn Coordinator
  - Older version called turn-and-slip indicator
  - Indicates a standard rate turn
    - 3° / second
    - May indicate a half-standard rate turn of 1½° / second in faster aircraft
  - Stops at about 45° of bank
  - Inclinometer
    - Slip / skid indicator – at base of turn coordinator instrument
    - Ball in curved glass tube
    - Indicates quality of turn
    - Not a gyro

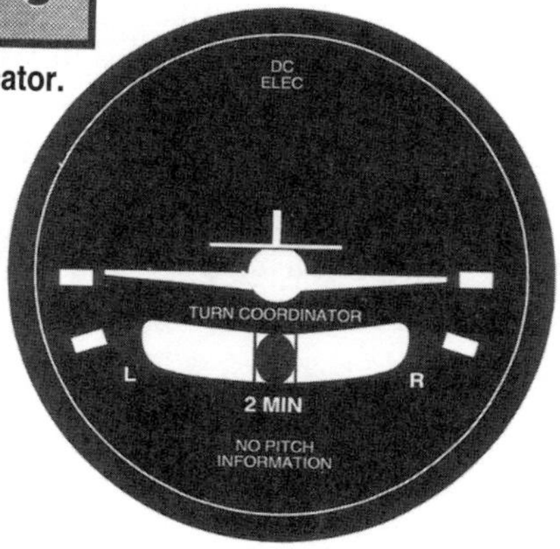

Figure 11-5. – Turn coordinator.

Pitot-Static System

- Instruments
  - Airspeed Indicator
  - Altimeter
  - Vertical Speed Indicator (VSI)
- Parts
  - Static Port (Source)
    - Measures pressure that is "static" (not moving) – the ambient air pressure
    - Located to avoid any burbling of the air and have the least disturbance
  - Alternate Static Source
  - Pitot Tube (pee-toe)
    - Measures impact, or dynamic, pressure (ram air)
    - Located to avoid disturbances
  - Static & Pitot Lines

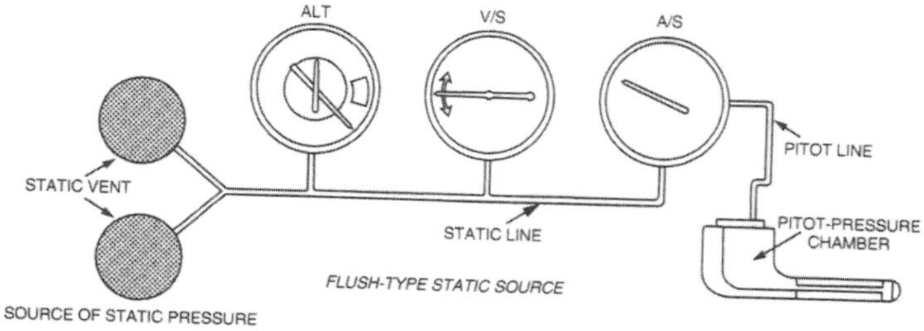

Figure 11-6. – Pitot-static system with instruments.

- Ports used
  - Static Port
    - Altimeter
    - VSI
    - Airspeed indicator
  - Pitot Tube
    - Airspeed indicator

Pitot-Static Instruments

- Airspeed Indicator
  - Measures the speed at which the aircraft is moving through the air
    - Measured in knots, MPH, or metric units
      - Knot = Nautical Mile per hour
      - 1 Nautical Mile = 1.15 Statute Miles
    - Measures the difference between the static pressure & impact pressure through a diaphragm

- Types of Airspeeds
  - Indicated – What is read off of the instrument
  - Calibrated – Corrections for installation errors
  - Equivalent – High speed compensation
  - True – How fast the aircraft is actually moving through the air

- Airspeed Markings
  - White arc – Full flap operating range
  - Green arc – Normal operating range
  - Yellow arc – Operations in smooth air only
  - Red line – Never exceed speed

Figure 11-7. – Airspeed indicator.

- Discuss the important V-speeds for the training aircraft with the student
  - V_{SO} – Stall speed in landing configuration
  - V_S – Stall speed in clean configuration
  - V_{GLIDE} – Best glide speed
  - V_X – Best angle of climb
  - V_Y – Best rate of climb
  - V_{FE} – Flaps extended speed
  - V_A – Maneuvering speed
  - V_{NO} – Maximum structural cruising speed
  - V_{NE} – Never exceed speed

- Vertical Speed Indicator
  - Gives an indication of climb or descent
    - Has a few seconds lag
  - An internal diaphragm and the instrument case are connected to the static line with a calibrated leak connecting the case to the line

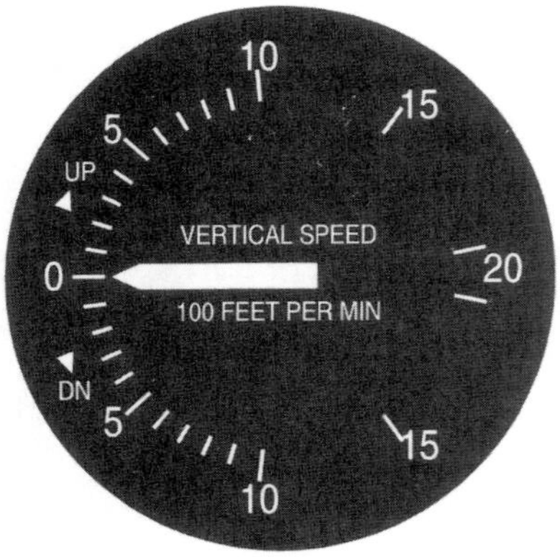

Figure 11-8. – Vertical speed indicator.

- Altimeter
  - Reports the height above a calculated pressure level (mean sea level)
  - Three pointers
    - 10,000
    - 1,000
    - 100 (20 feet)
  - Kollsman window

Figure 11-9. – Sensitive altimeter.

- Types of Altitude
  - Absolute (AGL) – Height above terrain
  - Indicated – Face of the altimeter
  - True (MSL) – Actual height above mean sea level
  - Pressure – Altitude above the standard 29.92" Hg plane
  - Density – Pressue altitude corrected for nonstandard temperature
- Altimeter Construction
  - Geared to aneroid wafers
    - More than one wafer means that it is sensitive
  - May have a temperature compensation spring
    - Cold means the true altitude is lower than indicated
    - Hot is vice versa

Electric Instruments

- Gyroscopic instruments may be powered by a vacuum / pressure system or they may be electrically powered
  - There may be a mix within an instrument panel
- Typical training aircraft will have vacuum attitude and heading indicators and an electric turn coordinator

Avionics Systems

- Aviation electronics
- These may consist of:
  - Annunciator panel
  - Radios
    - Communication
    - VOR
    - ADF
    - GPS
  - Radar
  - Auto pilot
  - HSI
  - Flight director
- Review the equipment installed in the training aircraft with your student

Deicing and Anti-icing Systems

- Anti-ice systems are designed to prevent the formation of ice
- De-ice systems remove accumulated ice
- For an aircraft to be certificated for flight in "known ice" conditions, it must at least have ice protection for the wings, propellers, and the windshield
  - Aircraft certified for flight in instrument meteorological conditions (IMC) must have ice protection for the pitot / static system
- Pitot / static heat is common on light general aviation aircraft
  - It uses an electrical resistance heater to warm the pitot tube and, on some aircraft, the static source thus preventing ice accumulation
- Wing Protection
  - Pneumatic de-ice boots are reinforced rubber devices attached to the wing's leading edges, and possibly to the horizontal and vertical stabilizers
    - Inflatable tubes within the boots expand to break up accumulated ice
  - Weeping wings use a perforated metal strip to pump a liquid solution over the leading edge of the wing
    - May prevent ice forming on the entire wing surface
  - Hot wings use a system of vents along the leading edge to provide the necessary heat to prevent ice formation
- Propeller Ice Protection
  - May use resistance heaters bonded to the propeller's leading edge or a weeping system
- Windshield Protection:
  - May use a heat based or liquid system

Magnetic Compass and Associated Errors

- Measures the earth's magnetic field
  - Seeks magnetic north
- Construction
  - Magnetic bars
  - Compass card
  - Pedestal
  - White kerosene
- Magnetic Compass Errors
  - Variation
    - Difference between magnetic north & true north
  - Acceleration & turning errors
  - Deviation
    - Errors introduced by the aircraft's magnetic field
      - Compass correction card

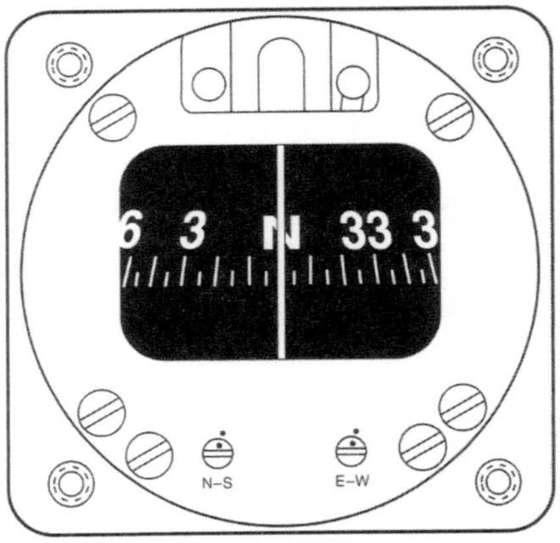

Figure 11-10. – Magnetic compass.

Maintenance Requirements

- Maintenance means the inspection, overhaul, and repair of aircraft
- Owner / operator responsible for maintaining in airworthy condition
  - Must ensure maintenance personnel have made the appropriate logbook entries

- Pilot responsible for ensuring in airworthy condition prior to use
- Preventative maintenance may be performed by a certificated pilot with a Private or higher – not with a Recreational certificate
  - Other maintenance requires maintenance certifications
- Types of Inspections
  - Annual Inspection
    - Required for all aircraft unless covered by another inspection program
    - Must be performed by an airframe and powerplant rated mechanic with inspection authorization
  - 100-Hour Inspection
    - Required for aircraft used to carry passengers or for flight instruction for hire
    - Must be performed by an airframe and powerplant rated mechanic
    - Annual inspection is also required and may substitute for a 100-hour inspection
  - Progressive Inspection
    - Approved inspection program used in lieu of a 100-hour / annual program
- Other Maintenance Requirements
  - Batteries used in the emergency locator transmitters (ELT) must be replaced (or recharged, if the batteries are rechargeable)
    - When the transmitter has been in use for more than 1 cumulative hour; or
    - When 50 percent of their useful life has expired
  - ELTs must be inspected every 12 calendar months
  - ATC transponders must be tested, inspected, and approved within the preceding 24 calendar months
  - Static systems, altimeters, and automatic altitude reporting systems, must be tested, inspected, and approved within the preceding 24 calendar months for certain operations

Service Bulletins / Airworthiness Directives

- Airworthiness Directives (ADs) are regulatory notices issued by the FAA requiring the correction or prevention of an unsafe condition found in an aircraft, aircraft engine, propeller, or appliance
  - Mandatory and have force of law
- The regulations require that a record be maintained showing the current status of the applicable ADs
  - This record is typically found in the aircraft logbooks
- Service Bulletins are notices issued by the aircraft manufacturer recommending a maintenance or procedural action
  - No force of law
  - May become AD

LESSON G12 – EMERGENCIES

Note to Instructor

- Review the following disclaimer with the student
  - The information below will discuss generally accepted procedures for handling emergencies and malfunctions both in the air and on the ground
  - These should only be considered guidelines
  - Follow the recommendations of the aircraft manufacturer whenever provided
  - Use the checklist if time permits

Emergency Procedures (AFM/POH)

- Keys to Handling Emergencies
  - First and foremost, FLY THE AIRPLANE!! DO NOT PANIC!!
  - Follow the recommended procedures
- Classifying Emergencies and Malfunctions
  - Annoyances
    - Malfunctions or conditions which will not endanger the flight
  - Urgencies
    - Malfunctions or conditions which may endanger the flight if not addressed in a timely manner
  - True Emergencies
    - Malfunctions or conditions which must be addressed immediately
- Reacting to Annoyances
  - Fly the aircraft
  - Review and follow the checklist
  - Ensure that the problem will not escalate
  - Land as required
- Reacting to Urgencies
  - Fly the aircraft and do not panic
  - Perform memorized tasks
  - Review and follow the checklist
  - Stabilize the problem to the extent possible
  - Land as required
- Reacting to Emergencies
  - Fly the aircraft and do not panic
  - Perform memorized tasks as time permits
  - Review and follow the checklist as time permits
  - Stabilize the problem to the extent possible
  - Land as required

- Cover the causes and required reactions for the following emergencies with the student, referring to the *Airplane Flying Handbook* and AFM/POH for the training aircraft
    - Engine Fire on Start
    - Smoke / Fire in Flight
    - Emergency Descent
    - Inadvertent Door Opening on Takeoff or in Flight
    - Split (Asymmetrical) Flap Condition
    - Partial Power Loss
    - Complete Power Loss
- Selecting a Suitable Emergency Landing Area
    - Always be alert for a suitable landing area
    - Airports are preferred in an emergency
    - Otherwise, find a field of sufficient size, within gliding distance
        - Open fields with no obstacles are preferred
        - Cultivated fields are usually satisfactory
        - Plowed fields may be acceptable landing parallel to the furrows
        - Roadways should be a last resort
            - This endangers others and increases the pilot's risk due to often invisible hazards
    - Plan to land into the wind if practical
        - DO NOT make any radical maneuvers to accomplish this
            - It is better to land downwind and under control than upwind and out of control
        - Obstacles may make a downwind landing more appropriate
        - It may be safer to land downwind and uphill than upwind and downhill
- Complete a thorough review with the student of the emergency section, typically section 3, of the AFM/POH for the appropriate training aircraft

LESSON G13 – AIRSPACE

Uncontrolled Airspace

- ATC services are not provided
- Class G airspace

Controlled Airspace

- ATC Services provided to IFR aircraft & VFR aircraft
  - Separation of Aircraft provided with ATC services
    - VFR aircraft may not be required to use ATC services
  - Traffic Advisories
  - Safety Alerts
- Types of Controlled Airspace
  - Class A
  - Class B
  - Class C
  - Class D
  - Class E

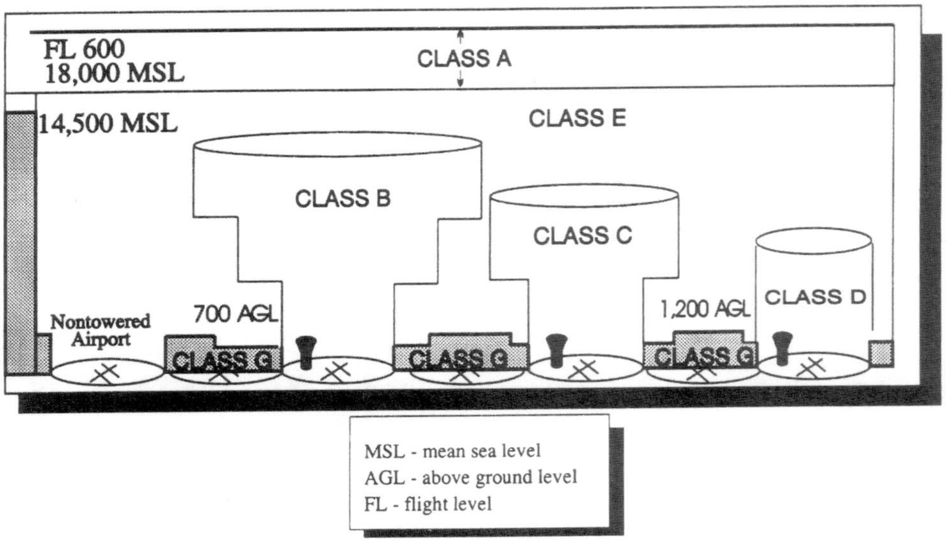

Figure 13-1. – Airspace classes.

Class A

- High altitude traffic and jet routes
- Including that airspace overlying the waters within 12 nautical miles of the coast, from 18,000 feet to FL600 over the 48 states & Alaska
- Not charted

Class B

- Surrounding the nation's busiest airports in terms of IFR operations or passenger enplanements
- Typical dimensions
  - Surface to 10,000 MSL
    - Exceptions are numerous (7,000 – 12,500)
  - Lateral dimensions are adjusted to the specific airport(s)
    - Contain all instrument approaches

Class C

- Airport with operating control tower, approach radar, and a certain number of IFR operations or passenger enplanements
- Typically, surface to 4,000 AGL

- Typical lateral dimensions
  - Inner circle – 5 nm radius
  - Outer circle – 10 nm radius
    - Altitude is generally 1,200 AGL to 4,000 AGL
  - Outer Area – 20 nm radius
    - Not shown on chart

Class D

- Airports that have an operational control tower
- Typically, surface up to and including 2,500 AGL
- Lateral dimensions
  - Vary at each Class D
    - 4 to 8 nm radius (mostly) plus extensions
    - Extensions
      - Class D
      - Class E

Class E

- Other controlled airspace including that airspace overlying the waters within 12 nautical miles of the coast of the 48 contiguous states and Alaska
- Lateral dimensions vary tremendously
- Vertical dimensions – for start
  - Surface
  - 700 AGL
  - 1,200 AGL
  - 14,500 MSL unless below 1,500 AGL
  - Other as indicated
  - Above FL600
- Types
  - Surface based (NAV, ATC, & WX)
  - Extensions (instrument approaches)
    - Imposes higher weather minimums than uncontrolled
  - Transition (700 & 1,200)
  - En route domestic areas
  - Federal airways
  - Offshore

Class G

- Dimensions vary
  - From the surface to overlying controlled airspace if controlled airspace does not start at the surface
- No ATC services

Special Use Airspace

- Prohibited Areas
    - Entry not allowed
        - Areas like around the White House
- Restricted Areas
    - Not allowed unless permission is received from the controlling agency
        - This is usually *not* ATC
    - Contains things like live firing!
    - Can fly in it when it is not active
        - This means the airspace has been released to the FAA
- Warning Areas
    - Contains the same hazards as Restricted, but is in international territory
        - Greater than 3 nm offshore
        - Can fly in it, but are forewarned
- Military Operations Area
    - Area of military activity that does not contain live firing
        - Can enter under VFR
    - Clearance is NOT needed
        - See and avoid
        - Military pilots may be doing aerobatics!!!!
- Alert Areas
    - Area of unusual activities & flight training
    - Keep your eyes open
- Controlled Firing Areas
    - Areas of operations which would be hazardous to nonparticipating aircraft if not controlled
        - Not charted
        - Spotters stop the firing any time an aircraft is near

Other Airspace Areas

- National Security Area
    - Areas where aircraft are asked to avoid due to the sensitivity of national security
        - May be expected to avoid entirely or at certain altitudes
        - This is voluntary
- Airport Advisory Area
    - Local Airport Advisory program
    - If an FSS is located on the airport (w/o a tower), the FSS will advise inbound and outbound traffic within 10 sm
    - Not charted

- Military Training Routes (MTR)
  - Special low level training routes for the military
  - In excess of 250 knots
  - Visual vs. instrument
    - IFR Military Training Routes (IR) – Operations on these routes are conducted in accordance with IFR regardless of weather conditions
    - VFR Military Training Routes (VR) – Operations on these routes are conducted in accordance with VFR except flight visibility shall be 5 miles or more; and flights shall not be conducted below a ceiling of less than 3,000 feet AGL
  - Numbering system
    - MTR's with no segment above 1,500 feet AGL shall be identified by four number characters; e.g., IR1206, VR1207
    - MTR's that include one or more segments above 1,500 feet AGL shall be identified by three number characters; e.g., IR206, VR207
    - Alternate IR / VR routes or route segments are identified by using the basic / principal route designation followed by a letter suffix, e.g., IR008A, VR1007B, etc.
- Temporary Flight Restrictions (TFR)
  - Generally a NOTAM restriction
    - Prohibited
    - Restricted
    - National security
- Parachute, Glider, Ultralight
  - Description and symbology on Sectional
- Terminal Radar Service Area (TRSA)
  - Similar to Class C but non-regulatory
  - Class D airspace surrounded by an area where ATC services can be and would prefer that it was provided to all aircraft

Cloud Clearance & Visibility Requirements

Airspace	***Minimum Flight Visibility***	***Minimum Distance from Clouds***
Class A	Not Applicable	Not Applicable
Class B	3 statute miles	Clear of Clouds
Class C	3 statute miles	500 feet below 1,000 feet above 2,000 feet horizontal
Class D	3 statute miles	500 feet below 1,000 feet above 2,000 feet horizontal
Class E *Less than 10,000 feet MSL*	3 statute miles	500 feet below 1,000 feet above 2,000 feet horizontal
At or above 10,000 feet MSL	5 statute miles	1,000 feet below 1,000 feet above 1 statute mile horizontal
Class G *1,200 feet or less above the surface (regardless of MSL altitude).*		
Day, except as provided in section 91.155(b)	1 statute mile	Clear of clouds
Night, except as provided in section 91.155(b)	3 statute miles	500 feet below 1,000 feet above 2,000 feet horizontal
More than 1,200 feet above the surface but less than 10,000 feet MSL.		
Day	1 statute mile	500 feet below 1,000 feet above 2,000 feet horizontal
Night	3 statute miles	500 feet below 1,000 feet above 2,000 feet horizontal
More than 1,200 feet above the surface and at or above 10,000 feet MSL.	5 statute miles	1,000 feet below 1,000 feet above 1 statute mile horizontal

Figure 13-2. – Basic VFR weather minimums.

LESSON G14 – CHARTS & PUBLICATIONS

Note to Instructor

- Ensure that a current local sectional and A/FD are available for this lesson
- Try to have a few advisory circular samples available for the student's review

VFR Sectionals

- Most commonly used
- 1" = 6.86 nautical miles
- Review the following with the student
  - Sectional Area of Coverage Page
    - Expiration date
    - Areas of coverage
    - Contour levels
  - Sectional Legend Items
    - Most explanations of legend items can be found directly on the legend
    - Many other symbols can be found in Aeronautical Chart User's Guide
    - Tick marks around airport symbols
    - Airport Data in detail
    - Navigation
      - Frequency boxes, including FSS frequencies
    - All the rest
      - Airspace
      - MTRs
      - Obstructions, Miscellaneous, & Topographic
  - Information Inside
    - Plotting direct route
    - Frequencies
    - Approach control facilities & frequencies
    - Maximum Elevation Figures
    - Special use airspace tables
    - Charting errors
  - Degrees, minutes, seconds
  - Where's our airport?
  - Where's the highest obstacle on the chart?
  - What else is around here?
  - Big white box on sectional shows coverage of Terminal Area Chart

Airport / Facility Directory

- Cover to cover
  - Effective dates and area covered
  - Back cover – index
  - Open-end pages index
- Contents / Abbreviations

- Additional information
  - Seaplane landing areas
  - Flight Standards District Office (FSDO) addresses and telephone numbers
  - Directory legend
  - Aeronautical chart bulletin

FAA Advisory Circulars

- The FAA issues advisory circulars (AC) to inform of nonregulatory material
- Unless incorporated into a regulation by reference, the contents of an AC are not binding on the public
- ACs are issued:
  - In a numbered-subject system corresponding to the subject areas of the regulations
  - To provide guidance / information on a subject, or
  - To show an acceptable method for complying with a regulation
- ACs are posted on the FAA's web site or are available by mail

Planning for Alternatives

- 14 CFR § 91.103, regarding preflight action, requires the pilot-in-command to become familiar with all available information concerning the flight prior to embarking
- For a flight not in the vicinity of an airport, the information must include "alternatives available if the planned flight cannot be completed"
- What does it mean to have an available alternative?
  - Having other airports to land at within a safe distance and with adequate fuel reserves
  - Having a plan of action if things don't go as originally planned
  - Being prepared for almost anything

LESSON G15 – AEROMEDICAL

14 CFR Part 67

- Prescribes the medical standards and certification procedures for issuing and for remaining eligible for a medical certificate
- Used by an aviation medical examiner (AME) to determine if a medical certificate can be issued

The Inner Ear

- Contains tiny semicircular canals
- The canals consist of tiny hollow tubes bent to form a half-circle
- Each tube is positioned approximately at a right angle to the other two canals
- Each tube is filled with fluid
- Acceleration, in any direction, sets the fluid in motion
- The moving fluid bends a mass of fine hairs near the expanded ends of each tube
- The motion of the hairs is transmitted via the vestibular nerve to the brain for interpretation as pitch, roll, and yaw
  - Sense of balance

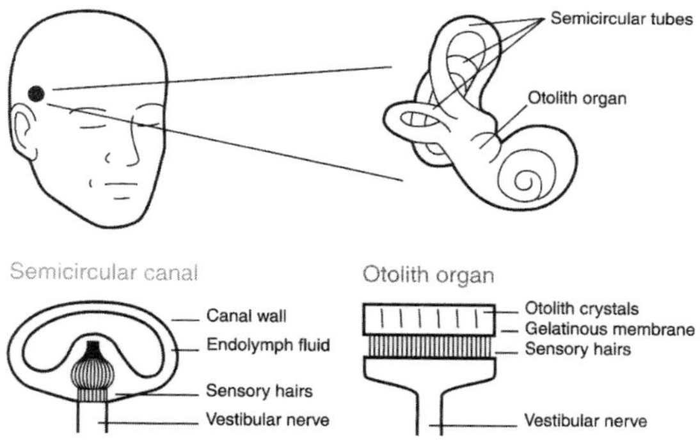

Figure 15-1. – Inner ear orientation.

Middle Ear and Sinus Problems

- The middle ear is the area between the ear drum and the inner ear
  - This area is vented to the external air pressure through the Eustachian tube which opens into the throat
- Sinuses are hollow cavities in the forehead and cheek bones
  - These are vented to the external air pressure through the nasal cavities
- The "vents" can become blocked and equalization can become difficult when influenced by an upper respiratory infection or nasal allergic condition
  - Do not fly with an upper respiratory infection or nasal allergic condition
- Ear Block
  - Normal pressure equalization for the middle ear is accomplished through the Eustachian tube by:
    - Swallowing
    - Yawning
    - Tensing muscles in the throat
    - Valsalva maneuver
  - Ear block occurs when congestion in the Eustachian tube prevents proper equalization
    - This can produce severe ear pain and loss of hearing that can last from several hours to several days
    - If not cleared shortly after landing, see an aviation physician

- Sinus Block
  - Sinus pressure equalization normally occurs automatically
  - Sinus block occurs when the small opening between the sinus cavities and nasal passages become blocked
    - Produces excruciating pain over the sinus areas, including the upper teeth
    - Bloody mucus may discharge from the nasal passage
    - If not cleared shortly after landing, see an aviation physician

Spatial Disorientation

- Lack of orientation with regard to position in space and to other objects
- Orientation is maintained through the body's sensory organs in three areas:
  - Visual (eyes)
  - Vestibular (inner ear)
  - Postural (nerves in skin, joints, & muscles)
- Conflicting information from the three areas may result in disorientation if not overcome

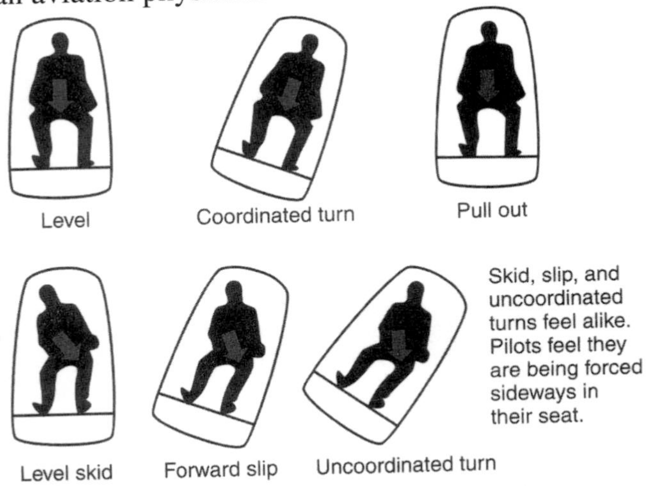

Figure 15-2. – Sensations from centrifugal force.

- Illusions in Flight
  - The Leans
    - May occur when a banked attitude is entered too slowly to set the fluid in the vestibular system in motion but an abrupt correction is used to level the aircraft which produces the sensation of a bank in the opposite direction
  - Coriolis Illusion
    - May occur when a pilot has been in a turn long enough to allow the fluid of the inner ear to stabilize, a movement of the head in a different plane of motion may cause the illusion of turning or accelerating on a different axis
  - Graveyard Spin
    - Recovering from a spin produces the feeling that the aircraft is turning or spinning in the opposite direction
      - Pilot either spins or turns the airplane back in the original direction
  - Graveyard Spiral
    - Observed loss of altitude will cause the pilot to increase the elevator back pressure to correct the situation
      - This tightens the spiral and increases the loss of altitude
  - Somatogravic
    - Acceleration on takeoff will give the illusion of a nose-up pitch attitude
    - Deceleration will give the illusion of a nose-down pitch attitude
  - Inversion
    - The feeling that the aircraft is tumbling backwards, caused by an abrupt change from climb to straight-and-level flight while in situations lacking visual reference
  - Elevator Illusion
    - The feeling of being in a climb or descent, caused by the kind of abrupt vertical accelerations that result from up- or downdrafts

- False horizon
  - Inaccurate visual information for aligning the aircraft caused by various natural and geometric formations that disorient the pilot from the actual horizon

The Eye

- The eye converts light to images which may interpreted by the brain as objects
- Light enters the eye through the pupil at the front of the eye and is focused on the retina at the back of the eye by a lens
- The retina transmits the image to the brain via the optic nerve
- The retina at the back of the eye contains two types of light-sensitive nerve endings
  - Cones
    - Distinguish color and distant items
    - Require considerable light to function
    - Clustered at the center of retina
      - Center of vision and daytime vision
  - Rods
    - Detect objects only in shades of gray
    - Can operate in very dim light
    - Concentrated in a ring around the cones
      - Peripheral vision and night vision

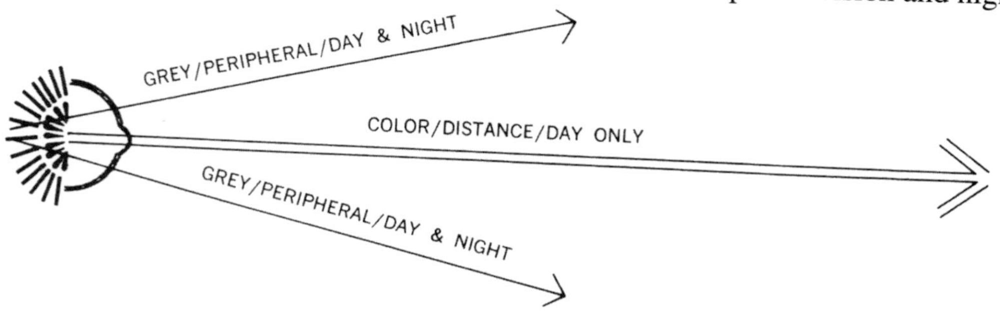

Figure 15-3. – Rods & cones in the eye.

Visual Illusions / Landing Illusions

- Runway width illusion
  - A narrower-than-usual runway can create an illusion that the aircraft is at a higher altitude than it actually is thus causing the pilot to fly a lower approach; a wider-than-usual runway can have the opposite effect with the risk of leveling out high and landing hard, or overshooting the runway

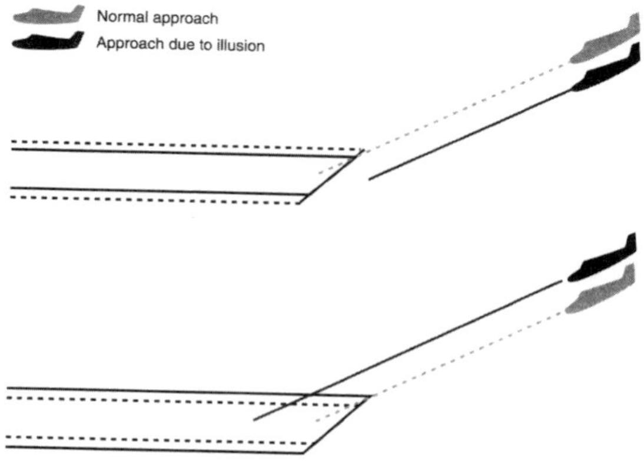

Figure 15-4. – Runway width illusion.

- Runway and terrain slopes illusion
  - An upsloping runway or terrain can create an illusion the aircraft is at a higher altitude than it actually is; downsloping runway or terrain can create an illusion the aircraft is at a lower altitude than actual
- Featureless terrain illusion
  - An absence of features such as an over-water approach or an approach over snow covered terrain can create an illusion the aircraft is higher than it actually is

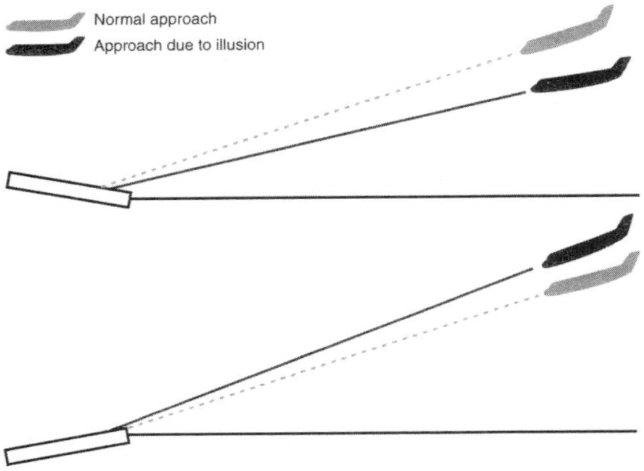

Figure 15-5. – Runway slope illusion.

- Water refraction
  - Rain on the windscreen can create an illusion of being at a higher altitude due to the horizon appearing lower than it is
- Haze
  - Atmospheric haze can create an illusion of being at a greater distance from the runway resulting in the pilot being high on the approach
- Fog
  - Penetration of fog can create an illusion of pitching up

Hypoxia

- Oxygen deficiency in the bloodstream that may cause lack of clear thinking, fatigue, euphoria, or unconsciousness
  - Caused by an increase in altitude
    - As altitude is increased, the amount of oxygen is decreased
  - Certain medications, smoking, alcohol, emotional stress, and the like, can cause the same effect at a lower altitude than normal

Carbon Monoxide Poisoning

- Carbon monoxide is a colorless and odorless gas that is 200 times more attractive to the hemoglobin in red blood cells than oxygen
  - Product of combustion found in exhaust or cigarette smoke
- The oxygen molecules required cannot attach to the red blood cells when carbon monoxide molecules are already present
- Symptoms
  - Headache
  - Drowsiness
  - Dizziness
  - Feeling hot
- Stop the flight and seek medical attention
  - Use oxygen if available

Hyperventilation

- Occurs when an excessive amount of air is breathed out of the lungs, such as when one becomes excited or undergoes stress, tension, fear, or anxiety
- Results in an excessive amount of carbon dioxide passed out of the body and too much oxygen retained
- Symptoms include:
  - Rapid breathing
  - Light-headedness
  - Suffocation
  - Drowsiness
  - Tingling Extremities
  - Coolness
  - Unconsciousness can happen

- Slow the breathing rate
  - Paper bag
  - Oxygen mask (with oxygen turned off)

Alcohol and Drugs

- The body requires about 3 hours to rid itself of the alcohol in one drink
  - 1 oz liquor
  - 12 oz bottle of beer
  - 4 oz wine
- Regulations require waiting at least 8 hours before flying after even one drink
  - Less than 0.04 percent by weight alcohol in the blood
  - No longer under the influence including hangovers
  - 12-24-48
    - Recommend 12 hours from bottle-to-throttle
    - No overindulgence within 24 hours of a flight; 24 hours is also the general rule with many commercial airlines
    - Studies have shown that some functions may require up to 48 hours for recovery following a "binge"
- Alcohol or a hangover can intensify the effects of hypoxia
- Prescribed and over-the-counter medications can severely impair a pilot's performance
  - Flying is prohibited while using any drug that affects the faculties in any way contrary to safety
- Safest way to approach it
  - Don't fly when taking any medication
    - Only fly if the medication was given by an AME with the instruction that it is safe for flying
      - DO NOT TRUST any non-AME MD for this recommendation

Stress and Fatigue

- A little stress can be good
- Too much stress can detract from ones ability to concentrate and make appropriate decisions
  - Everyday living can take its toll
  - Learning how to deal with stress can be key
  - Delay flight if the pilot is having a hard time dealing with the stress
    - Other people may notice it before you
- Fatigue is a depletion of body energy reserves, leading to decreased performance
- Acute fatigue – short-term
  - Adequate rest and sleep
  - Regular exercise and nutrition

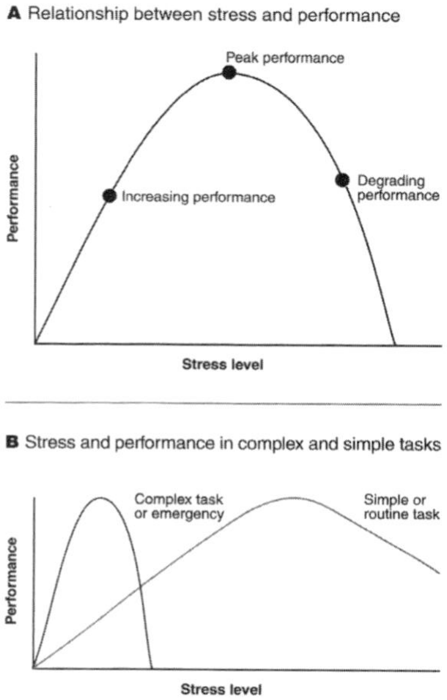

Figure 15-6. – Stress and performance.

- Chronic fatigue – long-term
    - Often has psychological roots
    - Consult a doctor
        - It takes time to recover

Dehydration

- Prolonged dehydration can impair judgment and may lead to debilitating conditions
- Contributors to severity may include:
    - Being in a hot and dry climate
    - Breathing dry air or oxygen at altitude
    - Being sick or sunburned
    - Wearing improper clothing for hot conditions
    - Intake of diuretics such as drinks with caffeine or alcohol
- Avoid dehydration while flying by:
    - Drinking plenty of water
    - Avoiding foods and drinks which promote the condition
    - Being dressed for the weather conditions

LESSON G16 – KNOWLEDGE TEST

Note to Instructor

- This version of lesson G16 is only for students pursuing a Recreational pilot certificate

Recreational Pilot Knowledge Test

- Ensure that the student is prepared for the knowledge test and passes the exam with an appropriate score
- Review any items missed by the student on the test

LESSON G16 / G1 – PRINCIPLES OF NAVIGATION

Effect of Wind in (1) Hour

- An aircraft, when airborne, becomes a part of the atmosphere and is directly affected by the wind
- An aircraft, in flight, is acted upon by two motions
  - The movement of the air mass in reference to the ground
  - The forward movement of the aircraft through the air mass

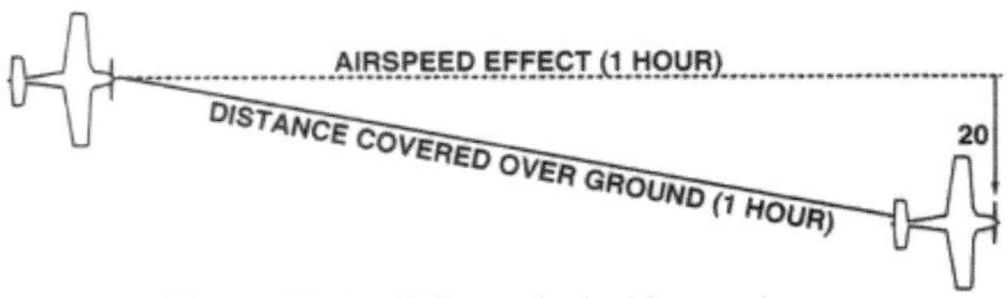

Figure 16-1. – Effect of wind in one hour.

- Assuming that no correction is made to counteract the wind's motion, an aircraft heading east at a speed of 120 knots in an air mass moving southward at 20 knots, will be 120 miles east of its starting point but 20 miles south of the desired point at the end of one hour

Drift and Drift Correction

- If the wind drift is not compensated for, the aircraft will not go where the pilot wishes
- Points to consider regarding drift correction:
  - On a flight from point A to B, pointing the nose of the aircraft in the same direction as the course, will rarely get the pilot to point B
  - Any wind blowing in a direction off the course line, will cause the aircraft to drift to the right or left of the course

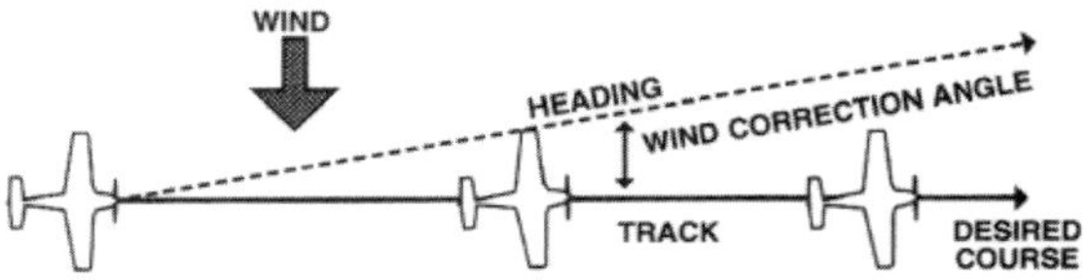

Figure 16-2. – Establishing a wind correction angle.

  - In order to fly from point A to B with a crosswind, the aircraft must be turned into the wind enough to prevent drift
  - While flying ground reference maneuvers, the drift or wind correction angle is typically determined by trial and error
  - For cross-country flight, trial and error is rarely acceptable

Various Types of Aircraft Speeds

- Airspeed – The speed of an aircraft relative to its surrounding air mass
  - Indicated Airspeed (IAS) – The speed shown on the aircraft airspeed indicator
    - This is the speed used in pilot / controller communications under the general term "airspeed"
  - Calibrated Airspeed (CAS) – The indicated airspeed of an aircraft, corrected for position and instrument error
    - Calibrated airspeed is equal to true airspeed in standard atmosphere at sea level
  - Equivalent Airspeed (EAS) – equivalent airspeed is calibrated airspeed corrected for errors caused by the compressibility of the air
    - This airspeed designation is not meaningful for the pilot flying slower / lower aircraft
  - True Airspeed (TAS) – The airspeed of an aircraft relative to undisturbed air
- Groundspeed – The speed of an aircraft relative to the surface of the earth
  - Groundspeed can be computed by the time required to fly between two points a known distance apart

- It makes no difference to the aircraft whether the air mass is moving or stationary
  - An aircraft's wings will generate lift
    - By moving through a stationary air mass
    - Or by an air mass moving over its wings

Latitude and Longitude

- The surface of the Earth is divided into an imaginary grid pattern consisting of parallels of latitude (East / West running lines) and meridians of longitude (North / South running lines)
  - Both latitudinal and longitudinal lines are needed to determine a precise location on the Earth
    - Measured in degrees (°), minutes ('), and seconds (")
  - There are 360 meridians of longitude – 180° East of the "Prime Meridian" and 180° West of the "Prime Meridian"
    - The "Prime Meridian" is the longitudinal line that represents the zero meridian and from which the East / West measurements begin
      - The "Prime Meridian" runs through the Royal Observatory, located in Greenwich, England, close to London

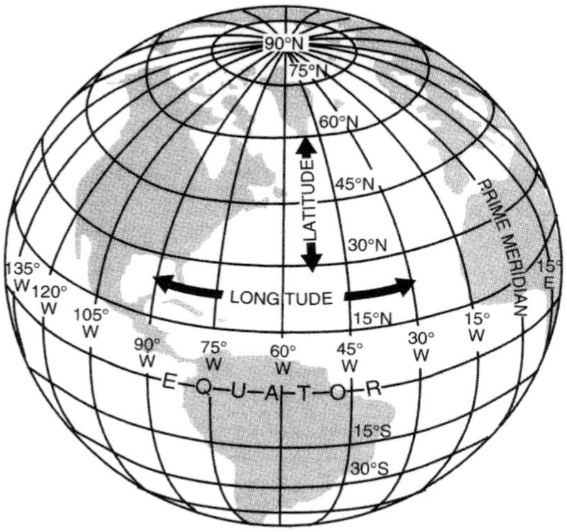

Figure 16-3. – Meridians and parallels – the basis of measuring time, distance, and direction.

  - The 180 lines running East and West are called parallels of latitude – 90 parallels to the north of the Equator and 90 parallels to the south of the Equator
    - The North Pole is 90° North latitude and the South Pole is 90° South latitude
    - These lines do not converge, but are parallel to each other
    - The Equator is the East / West line that divides the Earth into two halves and is the zero degree latitude line
    - Each minute tick mark, measured North and South between the parallels, represents one nautical mile
  - The United States is West of the "Prime Meridian" and North of the Equator
- With the system of latitude and longitude, any point on the surface of the Earth can be pinpointed

Earth's Magnetism

- The Earth has magnetic properties
- Around it, are magnetic lines of force running generally North and South
  - These lines of force are not straight, but curve this way and that depending on the composition of the Earth at various geographical locations
  - Because of the variance in the magnetic lines of force surrounding the Earth, and that True North and Magnetic North are not in the same location, variation compass errors occur

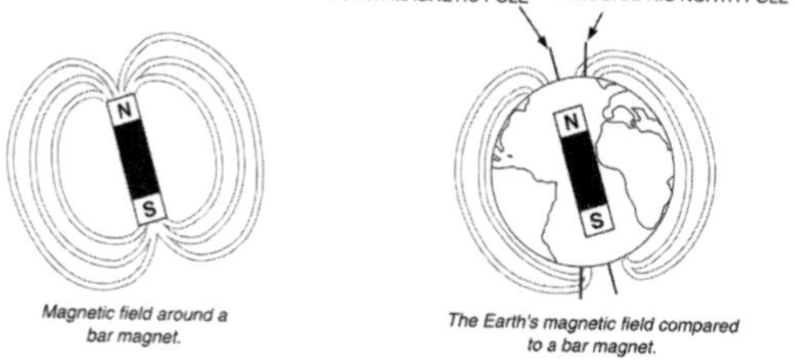

Figure 16-4. – Earth's magnetic field.

Variation – Isogonic and Agonic Lines

- Variation error – The angular difference between True North and the direction indicated by the magnetic compass, excluding deviation error
  - The compass needle does not point to True North but points to Magnetic North, located some 1,300 miles away
    - Magnetic north moves ever so slightly from time to time
  - Isogonic lines – equal angle – are drawn across aeronautical charts connecting points having the same magnetic variation

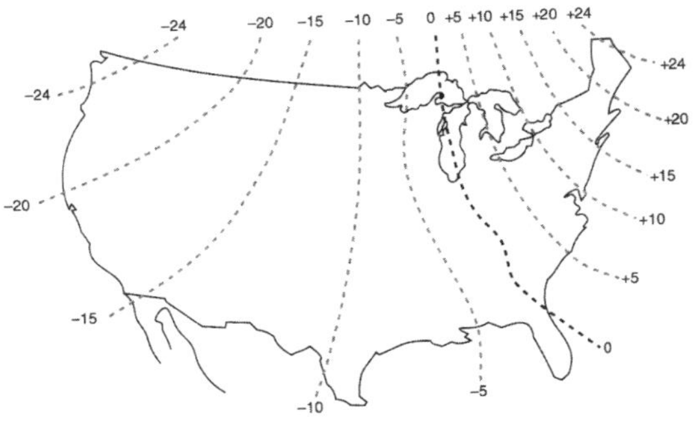

Figure 16-5. – Isogonic lines are lines of equal variation.

  - The Agonic line – no angle – connects points having no magnetic variation
  - VFR aeronautical charts show the isogonic and agonic lines
    - A rule of thumb for applying the correction for compass variation is, West is best (add) and East is least (subtract)

Magnetic Compass

- The magnetic compass is a self-powered instrument
- Since the magnetic compass works on the principle of magnetism, it is independent of the aircraft's pitot static system, electrical system, and vacuum system
- Besides the error of compass variation, the magnetic compass is prone to various other disturbances which must be understood for its proper use

Magnetic Compass Errors

- Deviation error is defined as the difference between the direction indicated by the magnetic compass not installed in the aircraft compared to its reading installed in an aircraft
  - Errors can be caused by the metal in the aircraft, and the electrical equipment operating in the aircraft
  - The direction that the aircraft is pointing may change the deviation error
  - The aircraft technician will reduce this error by "swinging the compass"
  - The pilot must make the final correction by applying the difference found on the deviation card
- Northerly turning error – a compass card dip error
  - Not apparent on a heading of east or west
  - If, on a northerly heading, the pilot turns the aircraft toward east or west, the compass indication will lag the turn, or show a turn in the opposite direction
    - When turning toward a heading of north, begin the rollout before the desired heading is reached

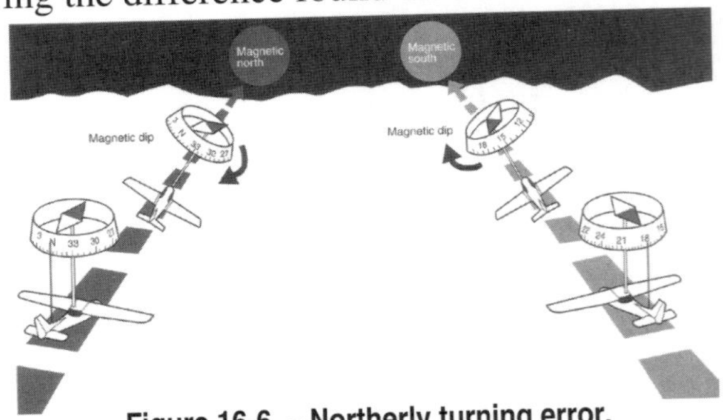

Figure 16-6. – Northerly turning error.

  - If a turn is made from south toward east or west, the compass will lead the turn
    - Turning toward a heading of south, wait until the compass passes the desired heading before beginning the rollout
  - N O S E – North, Opposite / South, Exaggerate

- Acceleration error – a compass card dip error
  - If the aircraft is accelerating or decelerating when on a heading of either east or west, the compass will indicate either a turn toward north or south respectively
  - *A N D S* – Accelerate, North / Decelerate, South
  - There is no acceleration error on a heading of north or south

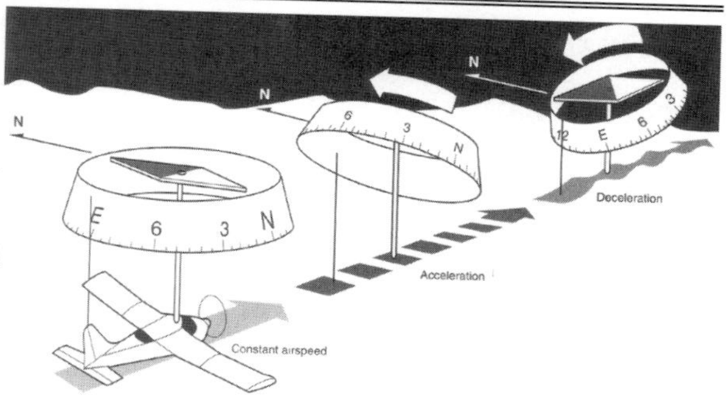

Figure 16-7. – The effects of acceleration error.

- Read the compass only when the aircraft is flying straight-and-level and is at a constant airspeed
- The compass is the best instrument to use to determine actual heading
  - The heading indicator is prone to gyroscopic precession
    - Adjust it to the magnetic compass every 15 minutes during the flight

LESSON G17 / G2 – PUBLICATIONS & EQUIPMENT

Aircraft Equipment List

- As stated in 91.205, the aircraft needs the required instruments and equipment for both day and night flight
  - Check in the aircraft's AFM/POH or A/C equipment list
    - There is an aircraft-specific equipment list for each individual aircraft
  - The aircraft equipment list includes required items for FAA certification, standard equipment items, and optional items
- Equipment obviously basic to airplane airworthiness such as wings, rudders, flaps, engines, landing gear, may not be listed and must be operative for all flights
- All items which are related to the airworthiness of the airplane and not included on the list are automatically required to be operational

VFR Sectional Chart

- Has a scale of 1:500,000 (1 inch = 6.86 nautical miles or 8 statute miles) which allows for more detailed information to be included on the chart
  - Sectional charts are printed on both sides
    - Instructions on the chart tell the pilot how to plot a course from one side of the chart to the other
  - The sectional chart is revised semiannually

Airport / Facility Directory

- Airport / Facility Directory (A/FD) is a 7-volume booklet series
  - It contains data on airports, seaplane bases, heliports, NAVAIDs, communications data, weather data sources, airspace, special notices, and operational procedures
  - A/FD is published every 56 days

VFR Terminal Area Charts

- Are helpful when flying near or in Class B airspace
  - They have a scale of 1:250,000 (1 inch = 3.43 nautical miles or 4 statute miles) which provides the pilot with more detail than the Sectional Chart
    - The terminal area chart is half the scale, twice the detail, of sectionals
    - They depict the airspace surrounding the busiest airports
  - Terminal charts display IFR arrival and departure routes
  - VFR terminal charts are printed on one side, with VFR routes on the other
  - The terminal area chart is revised semiannually

Plotter

- The aviation plotter comes in various shapes and designs
  - It is a combination of a ruler for measuring distance and a protractor for measuring direction (true course)

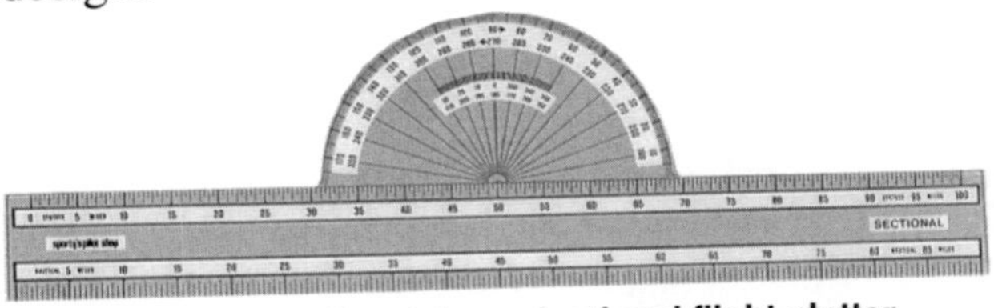

Figure 17-1. – Sporty's navigational flight plotter.

Flight Computer

Figure 17-2. – Sporty's electronic flight computer.

- A flight computer determines time, speed, distance, and fuel amounts
  - These computations can be calculated using math alone, however, it is much more convenient to use a flight computer, such as the E6B
    - The E6B may have other functions as well

Cockpit Management

- Thorough preflight planning and good cockpit management are necessary for a pleasant, efficient, and safe flight
  - Organize the charts in proper sequence according to their order of use
    - Charts that will not be used should be put away so they don't contribute to the cabin clutter
  - Fold the charts so that only the part used is in view
  - Place the chart, along with flight plan, on a kneeboard or a clipboard to keep them from being lost on the floor
  - Keep the plotter and flight computer within easy reach
  - Don't use the top of the instrument panel as a storage place
  - Pencil and note pad should also be kept close and secured
  - After using an item put it back where it belongs so it can be found when needed

Minimum Equipment List

- Minimum equipment list (MEL) procedures allow operation of an aircraft with specific items of equipment inoperative under certain circumstances
  - An MEL takes into consideration an operator's particular aircraft configuration, operational procedures, and conditions
    - It is the specific inoperative equipment document for a particular make and model aircraft by serial and registration numbers
  - The MEL must be derived from the master MEL (MMEL) for the aircraft type
    - MMELs for many aircraft are on file with the FAA
  - A letter of authorization is issued by the FAA for operation of the aircraft under the MEL
    - The MEL and the letter of authorization constitute a supplemental type certificate for the aircraft and must be in the aircraft
  - If an aircraft has an approved MEL, the aircraft must be operated in accordance with the provisions of the MEL

Supplemental Oxygen

- Per 14 CFR §91.211, no person may operate an aircraft at cabin pressure altitudes above:
  - 12,500 feet (MSL) up to and including 14,000 feet (MSL) unless the pilot(s) uses supplemental oxygen after 30 minutes
  - 14,000 feet (MSL) unless the pilot(s) uses supplemental oxygen
  - 15,000 feet (MSL) unless each occupant of the aircraft is provided with supplemental oxygen
- Additional regulations may apply to pressurized aircraft
- There is an increased risk of fire while using oxygen
  - Oils and greases may be more susceptible to catching fire
    - Do not use on oxygen equipment or fittings
  - No smoking!

- Oxygen system must be inspected according to the manufacturer's recommendations prior to use
- Types of systems
  - Diluter demand systems supply oxygen when the user inhales through the mask
    - May be used up to 40,000 feet
  - Pressure demand systems supply oxygen to the mask under pressure when above 34,000 feet
    - May be used above 40,000 feet
    - System may function similar to a diluter demand system at lower altitudes
  - Continuous flow systems are typically supplied to passengers or used by pilots in lower altitude situations
    - May use a simple mask or nasal cannula

LESSON G18 / G3 – CROSS-COUNTRY FLIGHT PLANNING

Applicable FARs

- Solo cross-country flight requirements (61.93)
  - Received required ground and flight training from an instructor
  - Demonstrated cross-country proficiency
  - Satisfactorily accomplished the pre-solo flight maneuvers and procedures required by §61.87
  - Solo flights may be made to another airport, within 25 nautical miles, if:
    - The student pilot has received training at the other airport
    - Received an instructor's endorsement
  - Repeated specific solo cross-country flights may be made within 50 nautical miles of the student's home base, provided
    - Instructor has given flight training in both directions over the route
    - Instructor endorsed the student's logbook
  - Endorsements for solo cross-country flight
    - Student pilot certificate endorsement
    - Logbook endorsement
      - Make and model of aircraft flown
      - Approval of preflight planning for route
      - Any limitations
- Pilot logbooks (61.51)
  - A student pilot must carry his pilot logbook and student pilot certificate
  - A recreational pilot must carry a logbook with instructor endorsements on all solo flights if:
    - They exceed 50 nautical miles from home base
    - Within airspace that requires communication with ATC
    - Conducted between sunset and sunrise
- PIC must become familiar with all available information concerning the flight (91.103)
- Minimum safe altitudes (91.119)
  - If an emergency ensues, the pilot must not be so low that it would cause danger to persons or property on the ground
  - Over any congested area, or over any open air assembly of persons, an altitude of 1,000 feet above the highest obstacle within a horizontal radius of 2,000 feet of the aircraft
  - 500 feet over other than congested areas
    - Over open water or sparsely populated areas, the aircraft may not be operated closer than 500 feet to any person, vessel, vehicle, or structure
- For a VFR flight, the aircraft must have enough fuel to fly to the first point of intended landing (91.151)
  - During the day, to fly after that for at least 30 minutes
  - At night, to fly after that for at least 45 minutes

- Information required on a VFR flight plan (91.153)
  - The aircraft identification number
  - The type of the aircraft
  - The full name and address of the pilot in command
  - The point and proposed time of departure
  - The proposed route, cruising altitude, and true airspeed at that altitude
  - The point of first intended landing and the estimated elapsed time until over that point
  - The amount of fuel on board in hours
  - The number of persons in the aircraft
    - Cancel flight plan with an FSS or ATC facility

- See Lesson G12 for basic VFR weather minimums (91.155)

- Special VFR operations may be conducted below 10,000 feet MSL within the airspace contained by the upward extension of the lateral boundaries of the controlled airspace designated to the surface for an airport (91.157)
  - Special VFR operations may only be conducted
    - With an ATC clearance
    - Clear of clouds

- While in VFR flight, more than 3,000 feet above the surface and below 18,000 feet MSL, maintain the appropriate prescribed altitude (91.159)
  - On a magnetic course of 0° through 179°, any odd thousand foot MSL altitude +500 feet
  - On a magnetic course of 180° through 359°, any even thousand foot MSL altitude +500 feet

- See Lesson G17 for supplemental oxygen requirements (91.211)

Measuring True Course and Distance

- Choose the most direct course possible
  - Check to determine that the terrain and airspace are free of obstacles

- Draw a bold line on the chart with straight edge from the departure point to the destination
  - If there is an obstructed area, use an intermediate landmark to bypass the problem, and continue with the planning

- Use the protractor part of the plotter to find true course (TC)

- Use the ruler portion of the plotter to measure the distance
  - For long distances, measure to an intermediate tick mark and add the measurements together

Picking Checkpoints and Altitudes

- Divide the flight into checkpoints roughly 20 miles apart
  - Checkpoints will help keep the aircraft on course and confirm its location
    - Choose prominent landmarks that can be easily identified from the air
    - Try to choose landmarks on the left side and not too far laterally from the course
    - Note the landmarks on the flight log

- Choose an en route altitude based on the hemispheric rule and other factors
  - When possible, it is a good idea to fly at a higher altitude
    - A higher altitude will improve the useful range of communication and navigation radios
    - Faster TAS for BHP
    - Improve radar coverage
    - Better view of terrain and landmarks
    - More time to troubleshoot and pick a safe landing site in case of an engine failure
  - Must provide adequate terrain and obstacle clearance
  - Must not violate airspace restrictions
  - Must be able to maintain VFR visibility and cloud clearance requirements
  - Must be appropriate for supplemental oxygen availability
  - Should provide best time for existing wind conditions
  - Should provide an adequate safety margin beyond the regulatory requirements

Pilotage

- Pilotage consists of noting prominent landmarks on a chart, locating them on the ground, and then flying from landmark to landmark
  - Pick easily identifiable landmarks
    - What looks prominent on a chart may be almost invisible from the aircraft
  - Landmarks used for pilotage would tend to be closer together than checkpoint selected for dead reckoning

Airplane Flight Manual / Pilots Operating Handbook (AFM/POH)

- Many aircraft manufacturers follow the General Aviation Manufacturers Association (GAMA) standard format for pilot handbooks
  - Section 1 – ***General*** contains measurements and descriptive data for the aircraft
  - Section 2 – ***Limitations*** contain items like: airspeed, powerplant, and weight limits
  - Section 3 – ***Emergency Procedures*** gives the airspeeds and checklists for emergency operations
  - Section 4 – ***Normal Procedures*** provides airspeeds and checklists for normal operations
  - Section 5 – ***Performance*** introduces performance problems and performance charts
  - Section 6 – ***Weight & Balance / Equipment List*** deals with weight and balance information and charts and has a comprehensive aircraft equipment list
  - Section 7 – ***Airplane & Systems Description*** discusses details relating to the aircraft systems
  - Section 8 – A***irplane Handling, Service & Maintenance*** includes topics on owner advisories, inspection periods, ground handling, servicing, fuel, and cleaning
  - Section 9 – ***Supplements*** expand operational procedures for both standard and optional equipment
  - Many AFM/POHs have an additional ***Safety Section*** covering various topics

Performance Calculations

- True Air Speed (TAS) is the speed at which an aircraft is moving through the air
  - It varies according to altitude, temperature, power setting, and engine performance
  - For flight-planning purposes, to find the TAS for the approximate altitude, outside air temperature, and engine rpm, check the AFM/POH for the aircraft being flown
  - The TAS, adjusted for wind correction and true course, yields estimated groundspeed

LESSON G19 / G4 – CROSS-COUNTRY FLIGHT PLANNING

The Wind Triangle

- The wind triangle, the pilot's version of vector analysis, is the backbone of dead reckoning
  - The wind triangle is a graphic explanation of the effect of the wind on the aircraft's flight
- By constructing a wind triangle the pilot can determine:
  - Groundspeed
  - Heading
  - Time
- A wind triangle is comprised of the following:
  - A line representing the direction of the track over the ground
  - A line showing the direction the aircraft is heading
    - Its length represents the aircraft's airspeed over one hour
  - A line showing the wind direction
    - Its length represents the wind velocity over one hour

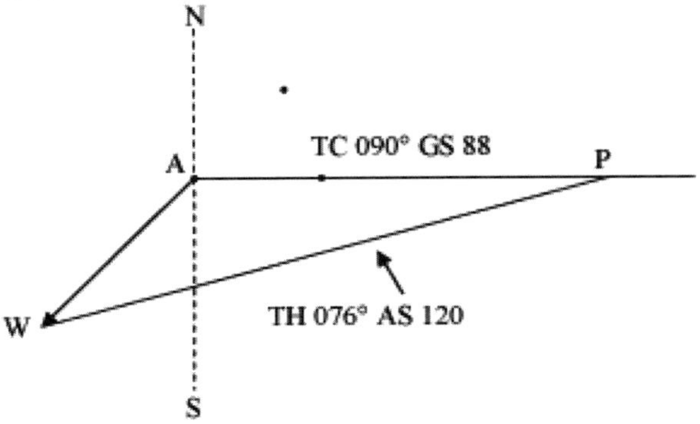

Figure 19-1. – Wind triangle as drawn.

- The following example will illustrate the concept and demonstrate the actual drawing
  - Suppose the aircraft is to fly from point A to point B
    - Draw a line connecting these two points on the sectional chart
    - Measure its direction with the plotter
      - This measurement represents the true course
      - For our example let's assume it is 090°
  - In the weather briefing, it was determined that the wind, at our intended flight altitude, will be 40 knots from the northeast (045°)
  - Further assume that the airspeed of the aircraft is 120 knots
    - On a plain sheet of paper, draw a vertical line representing north and south – label the end of the line "N" and "S"
    - Place the base of the protractor along the vertical line with the curved part facing east – the direction of flight
    - At the center point of the base of the protractor, mark a dot and label it "E", the point of departure
    - Along the curved edge, at 90°, mark another dot
      - This dot represents the direction of the true course
    - Also along the curved part, mark a dot at 45°
      - This dot represents the wind direction
    - With a ruler, draw a line from point "E" through the 90° dot out a few inches beyond the dot – label the line "TC 090°"

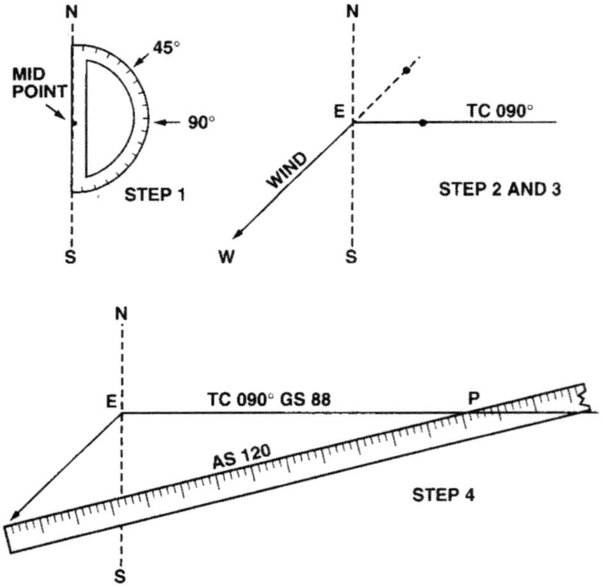

Figure 19-2. – Steps in drawing the wind triangle.

- Align the ruler with point "E" and the 45° dot and draw a line from point "E" and *away* from the 45° dot
  - This line represents the direction the wind is blowing
  - Label the end of this line "W", to represent the direction of the wind
  - In our example, this line is measured 40 units long, representing the 40 knot wind
    - These units can be in any unit length that is convenient
    - The unit of measure decided on must be consistent throughout the problem
- On the ruler, count out 120 units and mark this spot with a dot
  - Place the ruler so that the left end is on the "W" and the 120 unit dot intersects the TC line
  - Draw the line and label it "AS 120" and label its intersection point on the TC line as "P" for position of the aircraft after one hour of flight
- Measure the length of the TC 090° line from point "E" to point "P"
  - This measurement represents groundspeed in knots – in our example it would measure 88 knots (not to scale in Figure 19-1)
- The direction of the AS line represents the true heading – in our example this angle would measure 076°
  - To arrive at this figure, place the base of the protractor on the north-south line with its center point at the intersection of the airspeed line and north-south line
  - Read the true heading (076°) directly from the protractor
- The wind correction angle can be determined by subtracting 76° from 90°
  - Thus, the WCA for our example is 14° to the left

➢ This calculation is easier using an E6B flight computer

Dead Reckoning

➢ Dead Reckoning (DR) is defined in the Pilot / Controller Glossary as "…the navigation of an airplane solely by means of computations based on airspeed, course, heading, wind direction and speed, groundspeed, and elapsed time."
- DR can be both reliable and accurate
- Because DR involves many calculations, it is easy to make mistakes
- DR allows the pilot to calculate a position using elapsed time, true airspeed, wind direction and speed, and compass heading
- The word "dead" is actually corrupted from the term "ded", meaning deduced
- DR is often combined with pilotage for cross-country flying

➢ Navigation Sequence Formula:
- The basic sequence formula is, TC ± WCA = TH ± VAR = MH ± DEV = CH
  - Step One: TC ± WCA = TH (True Course ± Wind Correction Angle = True Heading)
    - Add right wind correction angle; subtract left wind correction angle
  - Step Two: TH ± VAR = MH (True Heading ± Variation = Magnetic Heading)
  - Step Three: MH ± DEV = CH (Magnetic Heading ± Deviation = Compass Heading)
- If the wind correction angle is not applied, use the following: TC ± VAR = MC ± DEV = CC (True Course ± Variation = Magnetic Course ± Deviation = Compass Course)

- Time, Speed, and Distance Formulas
  - Time = Distance / Groundspeed
  - Groundspeed = Distance / Time
  - Distance = Groundspeed x Time
  - Time conversion note: 6 minutes = 0.1 hour

Calculating Various Airspeeds

- There are three kinds of airspeed that the pilot should understand:
  - Indicated Airspeed (IAS) – the direct, uncorrected instrument reading obtained from the airspeed indicator
  - Calibrated Airspeed (CAS) – the indicated airspeed corrected for installation error and instrument error
    - Refer to the appropriate AFM/POH
  - True Airspeed (TAS) – the calibrated airspeed corrected for nonstandard pressure and temperature
    - To find TAS, use the flight computer to correct the calibrated airspeed for temperature and pressure variation
    - Estimate TAS: Add 2% of the IAS to the IAS for each 1,000 feet of altitude
- There is a fourth airspeed for those flying faster aircraft – Equivalent Airspeed (EAS)
  - EAS is CAS corrected for air compression

Electronic E6B Flight Computer

- These computers can handle from 10 to 40 computation functions
  - Most may be used for FAA exams
  - Many electronic E6Bs list the possible calculations on the screen and prompt the user for the necessary information
  - They also automatically transfer data – true airspeed, wind direction, and fuel burn – from one calculation to the next, minimizing the number of keystrokes to perform a series of computations
  - Most electronic E6Bs have a menu organization which reflects how a flight is normally planned and executed
  - The electronic E6B handles many unit related conversions
- Many of these devices incorporate timer and clock features

Figure 19-3. – Sporty's Electronic E6B.

Manual E6B

- The calculator side of the E6B provides the numbers and indices for rate, time, and amount on three different scales
  - The fixed scale represents amounts such as miles, speed, and gallons
  - The outer ring of figures on the rotating disk represents time in minutes and the inner circle of figures represents time in hours and minutes
    - To test the accuracy of the E6B, align the 10s – the 10 on the outer ring over the 10 on the inner ring and all of the numbers of both scales should be in perfect alignment
  - The triangular index on the inner ring, at 60 minutes, is the Speed Index
    - It's the reference for time, speed, and distance problems

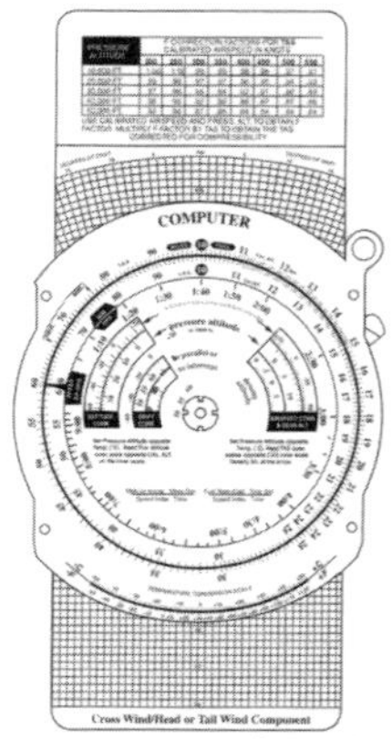

Figure 19-4. – Calculator side of manual E6B.

- Using the E6B requires common sense
  - The tool is based on the principle that Rate x Time = Amount
    - Rates can be speed or fuel consumption; time can be seconds, minutes, or hours; and amounts can be gallons or miles
  - The answer to a problem might be 15 on the outer scale but the operator has to determine if that number represents 1.5, 15, 150, or 1,500
- The E6B will perform a number of conversions
- The Wind Side of the E6B
  - Allows the pilot to account for the wind's influence on groundspeed and heading
    - Directions for these calculations are often printed on the E6B
    - The slide is inscribed with a radiating grid that denotes miles on the vertical scale and degrees left or right of the centerline on the lateral scale

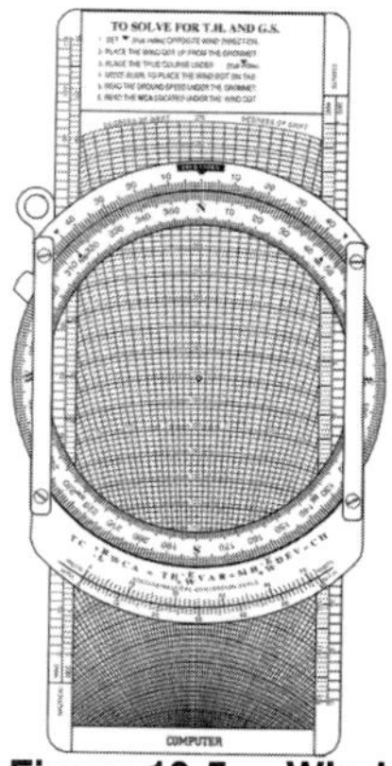

Figure 19-5. – Wind side.

- The wind side will compute more than just the procedures printed on the slide
  - It can also find the altitude with the most favorable winds
    - Work wind triangles for each altitude, and label the corresponding wind dot
  - It can also calculate an unknown wind and the radius of action
    - The radius of action is the time / distance an aircraft can fly out on a given course, turn around, and have enough fuel to make it back to the departure airport
    - Use this computation to know the point of no return when flying cross-country

LESSON G20 / G5 – CROSS-COUNTRY FLIGHT PLANNING

Diversion Procedures

- Diversions may be required because of adverse weather developing up ahead, an aircraft device failure, unanticipated airfield closure, or other reasons
- It is necessary to be able to quickly and safely plan the flight to a new destination
- There are many methods of teaching diverting to an alternate; the following is presented as one possible way to do it
- The mnemonic device "F2T2" stands for Find, Fix, Track, and Time
  - The pilot needs to know the aircraft's present position before starting the diversion
  - Establish a circular flight pattern around the known point and ***find*** the new destination airport
  - ***Fix it*** – Draw a line on the chart from the present position to the selected airport
    - With one corner of the flight plan form on the present location, place a pencil dot next to the alternate destination on the edge of the form
      - Place the edge of the form parallel to any meridian line and read the distance, by counting the tick marks on the meridian
    - Parallel the edge of the flight plan form or a plotter to the course line
      - Slide the form / plotter over to a nearby compass rose, without turning it and read the magnetic course to the airport
  - Estimate a new GS and WCA to destination
    - Determine time to destination and an ETA based on the time leaving the checkpoint
  - Having found and fixed the new destination, the pilot turns the aircraft onto a heading to ***track*** toward the diversion airport
  - Note the ***time*** of departure from the checkpoint to firm up the ETA and concentrate thereafter on good piloting technique
- The pilot should spend most of the time looking OUTSIDE of the aircraft throughout this process

Alternate Planning

- During the preflight preparation of the cross-country, it is important to locate all the airports in the vicinity of the flight in case of an immediate problem
  - Depending on the fuel available at any point along the course, choices may change
- Considerations for alternates
  - Weather expectations
  - Distance and direction from proposed course
  - Type of facility
    - Emergency equipment
    - Tower
    - Fixed base operator
    - Times of operation
  - Runway layout
    - Direction
    - Length
  - Physical properties of the alternate airport
    - Terrain
  - Traffic pattern

- Circle or highlight possible alternates on the sectional
- The pilot should jot down the information he wants to remember for each possible alternate

Lost Procedures

- To help ensure that becoming lost, to the point of necessitating a call to ATC, does not occur, prepare an "out" beforehand
  - Establish a bracket for the flight
    - Easily distinguished terrain features that, for the most part, parallel the intended course
- If the pilot does become lost
  - Don't panic
  - Do take time to evaluate the situation
  - Don't start backtracking and crisscrossing pointlessly in search of something recognizable
  - Don't tune the transponder to the emergency code, 7700, until told to do so
  - Do start the first 2 Cs of the 5 Cs – Climb, Conserve, Communicate, Confess and Comply
  - ***Climb*** to obtain a better view of the terrain while looking for familiar landmarks
    - Climbing also extends the range of radio communications
    - Having arrived at altitude, ***conserve*** fuel by reducing power and leaning the mixture
  - Continue on the present course
  - Make sure the magnetic compass and the heading indicator match
  - Look around outside at the terrain and compare this to what the chart shows
  - Check the map and flight log for the last known position and time
    - Estimate the distance flown from the last checkpoint
- Discuss the arc or circle of error methods of finding oneself
  - Once the location is confirmed, determine how to get back on course
- Describe the methods of using ADF, VOR, and GPS to find location
- Emphasize fuel concerns
- Put the last 3 of the 5 Cs into play
  - ***Communicate*** with ATC or FSS and ***confess*** the situation
    - Admit being lost, and don't withhold pertinent details
    - Tell the controller the aircraft's probable location
  - Finally, ***comply*** with the controller's instructions
    - The pilot should also tell the controller what he wants to do
    - The controller may ask the pilot a series of questions to help clarify the situation
    - The controller has a number of techniques to locate the aircraft
      - Radar
      - VOR orientation
      - Single-station fixing using VOR
      - It may also be possible to request Direction Finding (DF) through a FSS – this is not as common today due to the wide spread availability of better radar equipment
    - Once the aircraft's position is determined, the controller can get the aircraft back on course

LESSON G21 / G6 – AIRSPACE & COMMUNICATIONS

Class A

- Operation in this airspace requires:
  - An air traffic control clearance
  - Two-way radio communications
  - A transponder with altitude encoding capability
- Unless otherwise authorized, all aircraft must be operated under IFR

Class B

- Aircraft are required to have an air traffic control clearance before entering Class B airspace and must follow the basic procedures for communications and operations laid out in 91.129
- Equipment:
  - A two-way radio communications capability
  - An operating transponder with Mode C – see 91.131 (d)
- Besides the major or "primary" airport, smaller, "satellite" airports can be found within the Class B boundaries
  - When departing from a satellite airport within the Class B area, pilots must follow the tower instructions for departure, and then establish and maintain communication with the Class B controller while in the Class B airspace
  - If the satellite is a non-tower airport, pilots must contact the Class B controller as soon as possible after departure and maintain communication with the Class B controller while in the Class B airspace
- If the pilot doesn't hear the controller use the aircraft's N-number and say "cleared to enter the Class B airspace," ask for that clearance before crossing any Class B boundaries

Class C

- A Class C airport must have an operational control tower
- Serviced by radar approach control
- While not needing an ATC clearance to enter the airspace, the pilot is required to establish and maintain two-way radio communications
  - If the controller responds to a radio call with, "(aircraft callsign) standby," radio communications have been established and the pilot can enter the Class C airspace
- The aircraft must have an operating transponder with altitude encoding

Class D

- The pilot is required to have two-way radio communications capability and use it
- A transponder is generally not required
- Many Class D airports have part-time control towers
  - When the tower is not in operation, the airspace is reclassified as Class E or G airspace

Class E

- VFR flights are not required to have clearances or communicate with air traffic control
- A transponder is not required (except for aircraft operating within the 30 nautical mile Mode C veil around Class B airports or above 10,000 ft.)
- If the aircraft has a transponder, it must be turned on

Class G

- No communication with air traffic control is required and no separation is provided
- There are no clearance requirements
- There are no transponder / encoder requirements below 10,000 feet msl
- When flying in Class G airspace above 10,000 feet msl, the pilot must have a transponder / encoder, unless within 2,500 feet above the surface

Runway and Taxiway Signs, Markings, and Lighting at Tower Controlled Fields

- Refer to the *AIM, Chapter 2-Aeronautical Lighting and Other Airport Aids* for detailed discussion and diagrams

TRSA Communications

- Contact approach control on the publicized frequency
  - Give aircraft call sign, type aircraft, altitude, position, radar beacon code (if transponder equipped), destination, and request traffic information
  - Approach control will specify the time or place at which the pilot is to contact the tower on local control frequency for further landing information
    - On initial contact, approach control will assume that sequencing service is requested
  - Radar service is automatically terminated upon being advised to contact the tower
- Pilots of departing VFR aircraft are encouraged to request radar traffic information by notifying ground control on initial contact with their request and proposed direction of flight
  - Following takeoff, the tower will advise when to contact departure control
- NOTE: Much of the above discussion is valid for tower, approach, departure or clearance delivery communications

FSS Communications

- An FSS facility is identified on the sectional chart
  - Communication box is drawn with a heavy, blue line around it
  - A VOR or NDB facility, has the location of the associated FSS under its info box in brackets
- The pilot can communicate with the FSS on the universal FSS frequency of 122.2 MHz and the universal emergency frequency, 121.5 MHz
- Frequencies listed above the box are for that particular FSS only
  - If there is an "R" after the frequency, it means the FSS can receive only on that frequency
- Many FSSs are equipped with Remote Communications Outlets (RCOs) and can transmit on the same frequency at more than one location
- Discuss the FSS communications process with the student
  - Remember the 4 W's

- Besides receiving weather information, the pilot can take care of other business as well through the FSS
  - The pilot can receive local NOTAMs for an alternate airport, amend a flight plan, and get a frequency for flight following (radar services)
  - FSS will relay PIREPs to the pilot as well
    - Take the time to report a PIREP if the situation warrants it

Tower Communications

- A control tower issues takeoff and landing clearances and coordinates traffic flow for all aircraft movements on the airport
- On reaching the departure runway, or when ready for takeoff, switch to the tower frequency
  - Monitor ground or tower while performing before takeoff checks
  - When ready for takeoff, use the 4 W's format for initial call-up to the tower
- Because of traffic complications, the controller may not be ready to clear you for takeoff
  - Always repeat the clearance back to the controller, to ensure it is correct
  - Ultimately, the controller will clear the aircraft for takeoff
  - Respond with a read-back
  - Visually clear final approach before taxiing onto the runway

Approach Control

- Approach Control is responsible for directing traffic into airport terminal areas
- Frequencies are noted on VFR and IFR charts
- Review the *AIM, Chapter 3-Airspace* and *Chapter 4-Air Traffic Control*

Departure Control

- Departure Control is responsible for directing traffic out of airport terminal areas
- The proper frequency is noted on VFR and IFR charts
- After takeoff from a Class C or B airport, the tower will tell the pilot when to contact departure control
  - Read back the frequency
  - Tune the frequency and listen to make sure it is clear before transmitting
  - The departure controller will make traffic advisories and issue heading or altitude changes as necessary
  - On exiting the departure controller's airspace, the controller will release the pilot
- Review the AIM, Chapter 3-Airspace and Chapter 4-Air Traffic Control

Clearance Delivery

- Most busy airports, usually Class B or C, have a Clearance Delivery frequency
- Before calling ground control, monitor ATIS, and then contact the Clearance Delivery controller to request and receive a VFR departure route, altitude, and clearance
  - Use the 4 W's
- The controller's clearance will most likely include instructions on heading and altitude to fly, as well as a squawk code
  - Write this information down and read back the clearance information

Ground Control

- Ground Control exists at an airport with a control tower
  - The ground controller is responsible for the movement of aircraft on the surface
- Most ground control frequencies begin with the numerals 121
  - If the tower instructs the pilot to, *"contact ground point niner,"* he means 121.9 MHz
- The ground control frequency appears on the back of the chart with the airport listings and in the A/FD
- After speaking with clearance delivery, contact ground control
  - Use the 4 W's
- The ground controller will give a taxi clearance, possibly including hold short information
  - Read it back

ATC Light Gun Signals

Color and Type of Signal	*Aircraft on the Ground*	*Aircraft in Flight*
Steady green	Cleared for takeoff	Cleared to land
Flashing green	Cleared for taxi	Return for landing (to be followed by steady green at the proper time)
Steady red	STOP	Give way to other aircraft and continue circling
Flashing red	Taxi clear of the runway in use	Airport unsafe, do not land
Flashing white	Return to starting point on airport	Not applicable
Alternating red and green	Exercise extreme caution	Exercise extreme caution

LESSON G22 / G7 – ELECTRONIC AIDS TO NAVIGATION

VOR Tuning and Identifying

- VOR is the common term for VHF Omni-directional Range
- A VOR is a ground based radio transmitter projecting straight line courses (line-of-sight) in all directions from the station
- A VOR's operating frequency range is between 108.0 to 117.95 MHz

Figure 22-1. – VOR ground station.

- The distance that a radial is projected from the station depends on the strength of the signal as well as the terrain surrounding the station
- Find the VOR on the sectional chart
  - Tune the VOR receiver to the indicated frequency
    - Review this operation for the training aircraft's radio
  - Positively identify the VOR station by its voice or Morse code identifier

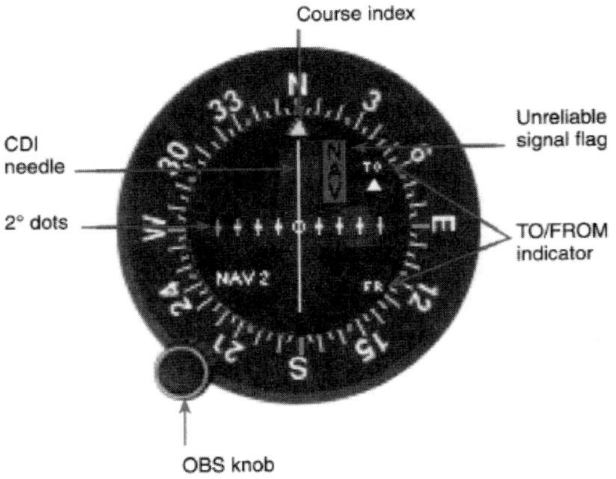

Figure 22-2. – VOR indicator.

VOR Intercepting and Tracking

- Discuss the parts of the VOR head with the student
- Use figures below to discuss the following:
  - Finding the current radial
  - Intercepting a particular course to the VOR
  - Tracking inbound to the station
  - Station passage
  - Intercepting and tracking an outbound radial

To intercept a course of 025°, inbound of VOR A:

1. Present position, inbound on 160 radial.
2. Turn right to parallel inbound course. 025° – 180° = 205°, 205 – 160 = 45° (double 45 for interception angle of 90°). Turn to 295° (205° + 90°).
3. Maintain heading of 295° until 205 radial is intercepted (OBS 025, needle centered).
4. Track inbound on 205 radial.

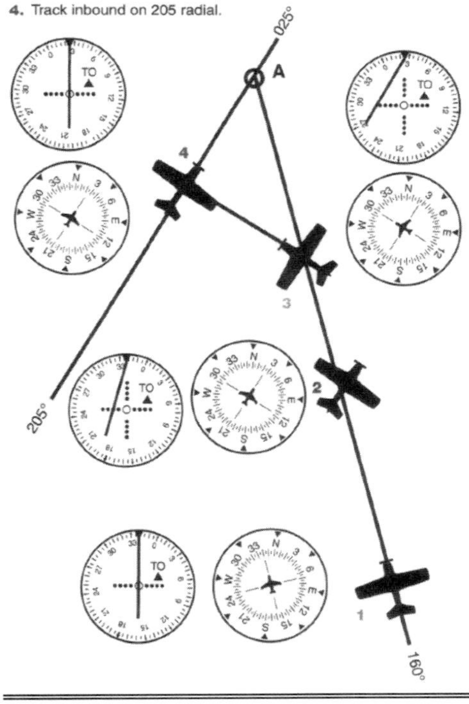

Figure 22-3. – VOR course interception.

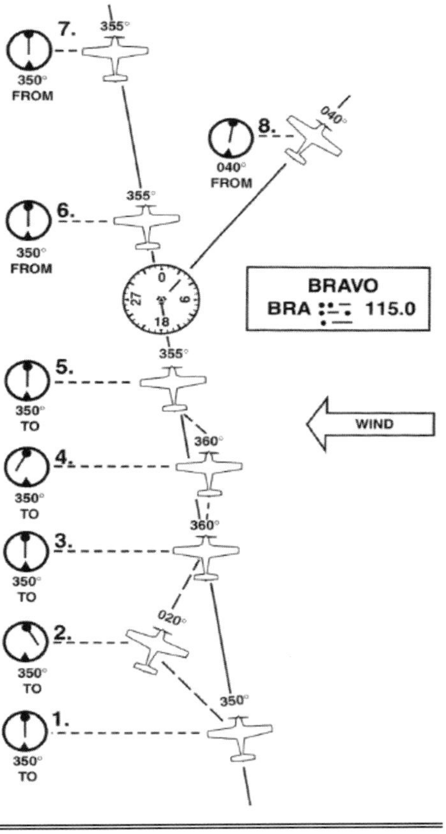

Figure 22-4. – Tracking a radial in a crosswind.

ADF / NDB Tuning and Identifying

Figure 22-5. – ADF indicator.

- ADF (Automatic Direction Finder) is a radio receiver with its companion ADF dial, that allows the pilot to fly to or away from an NDB (Non-Directional Beacon)
  - An NDB is a ground based radio station operating on a low or medium radio frequency of 200 to 415 kHz
  - An ADF receiver can also tune the AM stations in the commercial radio band
- Find the desired NDB facility on the sectional chart
  - Tune the ADF receiver to the indicated frequency
    - Review this operation for the training aircraft's radio
  - Positively identify the NDB station by its Morse code identifier

ADF / NDB Homing

- Homing is defined as flying the aircraft to the NDB station without compensating for crosswind
- Generally, homing will cause the aircraft to fly a curved path over the ground to the station
- To home to the station, the pilot keeps the ADF needle on its 12 o'clock position

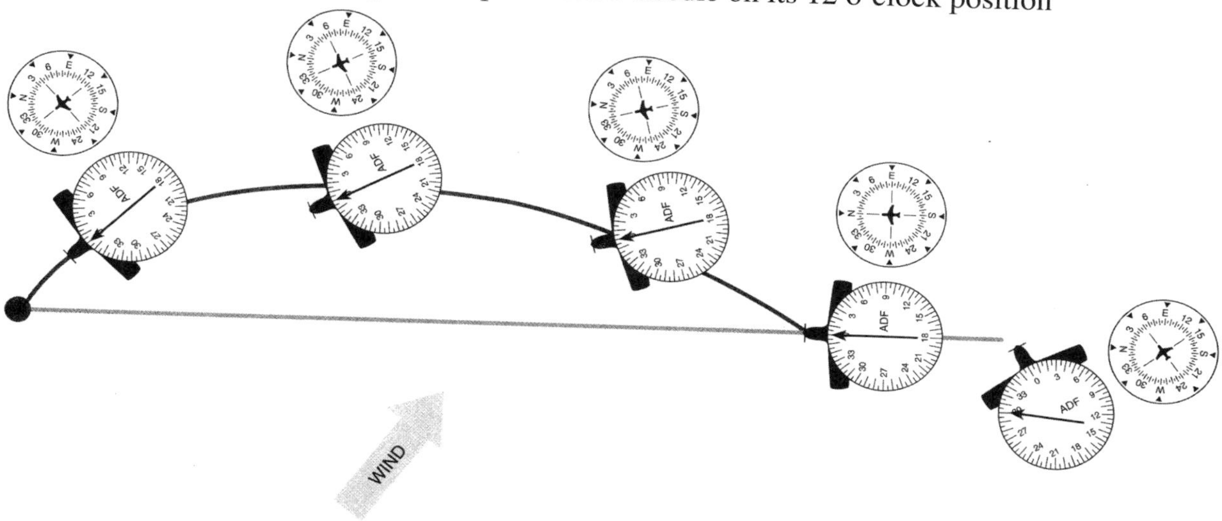

Figure 22-6. – ADF homing with crosswind.

ADF / NDB Intercepting and Tracking

➢ Use the figures below to discuss tracking inbound and outbound with the student

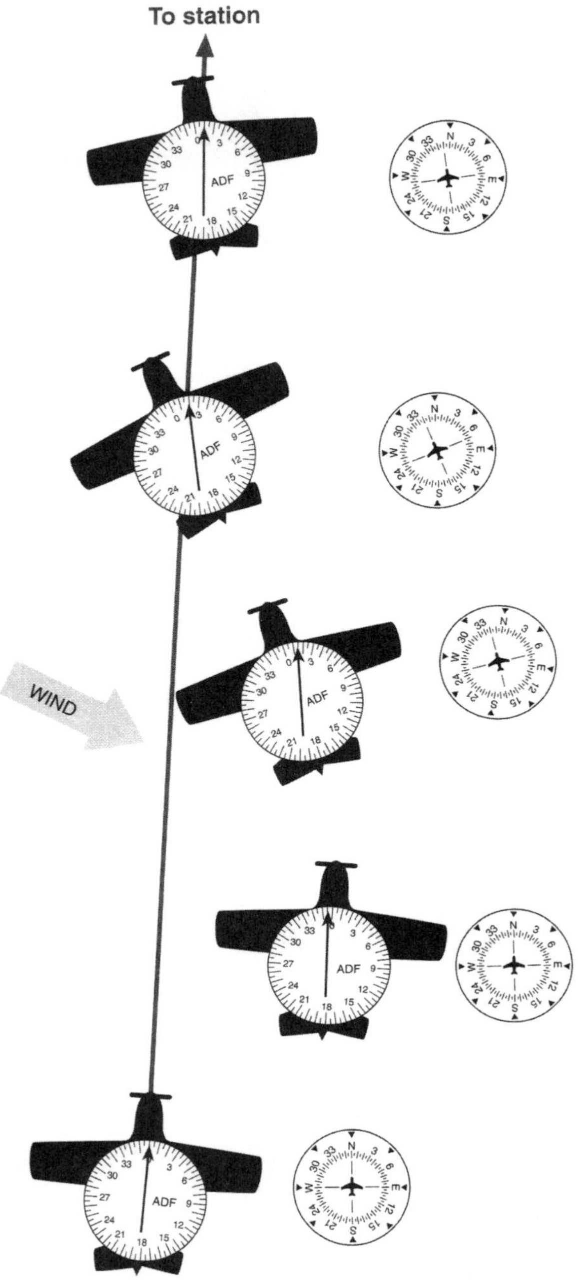

Figure 22-7. – ADF tracking inbound.

Figure 22-8. – ADF interception and tracking outbound.

ADF / NDB Errors

➢ An ADF radio receiver is susceptible to interference, especially from lightning
- The needle on the ADF's dial may point to a lightning discharge rather than to the station

➢ Failure to identify the station after tuning in a frequency
- It is easy to dial in the wrong station, see the ADF needle swing and settle on a position, and believe the correct NDB is being received

➢ Homing, in a curved path, to the NDB when a straight track is desired

- Over controlling track corrections close to the station (chasing the needle)
- Failure to ensure that the directional gyro agrees with the magnetic compass
  - Check prior to using the ADF for tracking and every 15 minutes thereafter
- Failure to turn the aircraft more than the degrees necessary to intercept
- Trying to track the course before intercepting the bearing
  - The opposite error occurs when the pilot continues to fly the intercept angle after it is time to turn and start tracking

LESSON G23 / G8 – INSTRUMENT FLYING

Basic Attitude Instrument Flying

- Basic instrument flight training is meant to give the non-instrument rated pilot the ability to handle the aircraft safely for a limited time
  - On entering unexpected adverse weather
  - When encountering conditions of IFR while night flying or flying over a large body of water
- A non-instrument rated pilot *must not* use this level of instruction to fly into instrument conditions
  - If the VFR pilot is caught in instrument conditions, he should call the nearest FSS or ATC facility and follow their instructions after making the 180° turn back toward VFR weather and establishing a stable flight condition
- The pilot must acquire three fundamental skills: instrument cross-check, instrument interpretation, and aircraft control
- Flight Instruments and Procedures
  - There are four flight attitudes; straight-and-level, turns, climbs, and descents
    - Control of the these four attitudes is accomplished by:
      - Pitch control
      - Bank control
      - Power control
  - Discuss the instruments below with the student
    - Attitude Indicator
      - The attitude indicator shows both pitch and bank and is the primary instrument to indicate aircraft attitude for the VFR pilot
    - Heading Indicator
    - Altimeter
    - Vertical Speed Indicator
    - Airspeed Indicator
    - Turn Coordinator
- The basic performance formula for attitude instrument flying, as well as flying by visual outside reference, is: POWER + ATTITUDE = PERFORMANCE

➢ Use the included diagrams, the *Airplane Flying Handbook*, and the performance formula to discuss the following BAI maneuvers:

- Straight-and-level

- Turns to headings

- Straight descents and descending turns

- Straight climbs and turning climbs

Instrument Scan and Cross-check

- ➢ The FAA uses the terms cross-checking and scanning as synonyms
- ➢ The pilot cross-checks the flight instruments by scanning his eyes over them in a logical and meaningful way depending on what information he is seeking

- Two Methods of scan:
  - Primary / Supporting Scan
  - Control / Performance Scan
- Emphasize the Control / Performance Scan with its underlying principle of POWER + ATTITUDE = PERFORMANCE with the student
  - Control Instruments
    - The control instruments display immediate attitude and power indications
      - In the control / performance scan technique, the tachometer, manifold pressure, and/or fuel flow setting (depending on the aircraft) establishes power and the attitude indicator yields attitude
    - Make all flight control inputs with reference to the attitude indicator
  - Performance Instruments
    - The performance instruments become supportive to the attitude indicator
      - Heading Indicator
      - Altimeter
      - Vertical Speed Indicator
      - Airspeed Indicator
      - Turn Coordinator (turn and bank)
    - They are considered as either primary or secondary depending on the attitude established
  - Navigation Instruments
    - The third group of instruments is the navigation instruments
- In scanning the instruments, the pilot must not become fixated on any one instrument
  - The pilot scans the instruments to cross-check one instrument against the other
- Discuss the selected radial cross-check pattern with the student using the figure below

Unusual Flight Attitude (Nose-High) Recovery

➢ Discuss recovery from a nose high unusual attitude with the student using the figure below

Unusual Flight Attitude (Nose-Low) Recovery

➢ Discuss recovery from a nose low unusual attitude with the student using the figure below

Full Panel Instrument Flying

➢ Refer to above *Basic Attitude Instrument Flight* for this discussion

Partial Panel Instrument Flying

➢ Discuss types and recognition of failures with the student including vacuum, pitot-static, and electrically related problems

➢ Discuss alternative instruments to scan with each type of failure

LESSON G24 / G9 – CROSS-COUNTRY FLIGHT PLANNING EXERCISE

Cross-Country Planning Exercise

- The student should use the knowledge and skills learned in the previous lessons to plan a cross-country flight near the maximum range of the training aircraft

LESSON G25 / G10 – NIGHT FLYING

Night Flying Overview

- Night flight training is required for a private pilot certificate
- Many aspects of flying at night are different from daytime flying
  - Aircraft inspection is more difficult
  - The cockpit becomes unfamiliar in the absence of bright light
  - Weather considerations, flight planning, and cockpit organization are more critical
  - Animals on the runway are more difficult to see at night
- After acquiring the necessary skills, many pilots prefer night flying to day
  - The lack of thermal activity results in smoother air and reduced turbulence
  - The pilot will encounter much less traffic
  - Navigation is simpler – not as many landmarks are visible

The Eye

- Vision changes depending on available light
  - Light enters the eye by passing through the cornea (outer layer) and lens which focuses the image on the retina
    - The retina converts the visual image into electrical energy, which is sent to the brain
  - Two types of photosensitive cells cover the retina called rods and cones
    - Cones are sensitive mostly to colors and depend on daylight for their proper operation
      - Cones don't function in dim light
      - Most of the cones are located in the center of the eye, called the fovea
        - The fovea affords us our best forward vision in daylight
    - At night, central vision cannot function well because the rods, which are responsible for light reception, are more concentrated in a ring around the cones
      - Rods "see" objects only in shades of gray
      - Objects at night are seen more clearly through peripheral vision

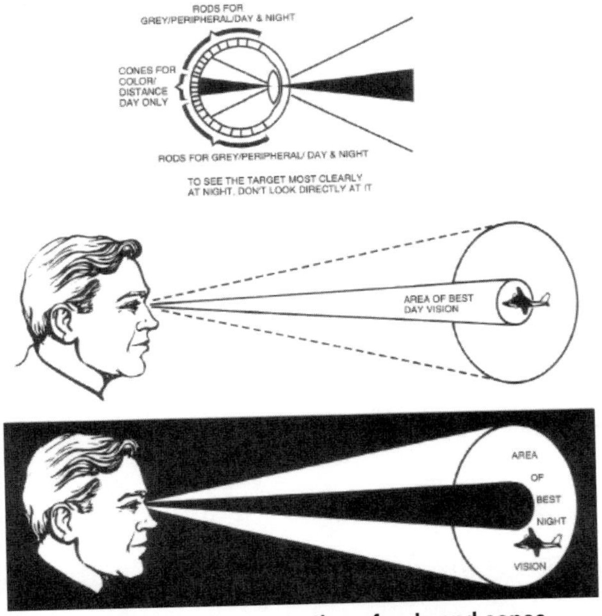

Figure 25-1.—Concentration of rods and cones determine how we see day and night.

Applicable FARs

- A student pilot may not operate an aircraft in solo flight at night unless (61.87)
  - Has had the appropriate flight training at night
  - Has received navigation training at night in the vicinity of the airport
  - An endorsement in the student's logbook within 90 days preceding the flight

- The private pilot candidate needs 3 hours of night flight training in a single-engine airplane including (61.109)
  - One cross-country flight of over 100 nautical miles total distance
  - 10 takeoffs and 10 landings to a full stop
    - Each landing involving a flight in the traffic pattern at an airport
- To carry passengers at night, (1 hour after sunset to 1 hour before sunrise) within the preceding 90 days, the pilot must make at least three takeoffs and three landings to a full stop (61.5)
  - As sole manipulator of the flight controls
  - In an aircraft of the same category, class, and type (if type rating is required)
- From sunset to sunrise (91.209)
  - No one may operate an aircraft unless it has lighted position lights
  - No one may park or move an aircraft unless it
    - Is clearly illuminated
    - Has lighted position lights
    - Is in an area that is marked by obstruction lights
  - If an aircraft is equipped with anticollision lights, they must be turned on unless the pilot determines that it would be safer to turn the lights off
- Different VFR visibility and cloud clearance requirements exist when below 10,000 feet MSL and when close to the surface in uncontrolled airspace at night (91.155)

Airspace	***Flight Visibility***	***Distance From Clouds***
Class G: NIGHT 1,200 ft. or less above surface (regardless of MSL altitude) and more than 1,200 feet above the surface but less than 10,000 feet MSL	3 statute miles	500 feet below 1,000 feet above 2,000 feet horizontal

Figure 25-2. – Night VFR visibility and cloud clearances.

- If a pilot is in class G airspace below 1,200 feet AGL and remains in the traffic pattern (within ½ mile of the runway), he can fly in visibilities of 1 statue mile and clear of clouds
- Review §91.205-c concerning aircraft equipment for VFR at night

Night Illusions

- There are some 14 illusions leading the pilot to spatial disorientation
  - Most of these illusions are generated from sensations caused by the vestibular system located in the inner ear and are discussed in Lesson G15 – *Aeromedical*
- The following three night related illusions may lead to landing errors
  - Autokinesis – In the dark, a static light will appear to move about when stared at for many seconds
  - Featureless terrain illusion – An absence of ground features, as when landing over darkened areas, can create the illusion that the aircraft is at a higher altitude than it actually is

- Ground lighting illusions
  - Lights along a straight path, such as a road, and even lights on moving trains can be mistaken for runway and approach lights
  - Bright runway and approach lighting systems, especially where few lights illuminate the surrounding terrain, may create the illusion of less distance to the runway

➢ Other causes of illusions to consider when flying at night:
- On clear nights, distant, stationary lights can be mistaken for stars or other aircraft
- Dark nights eliminate reference to a horizon and the pilot must rely more on flight instruments than outside references to maintain spatial orientation
- Flicker vertigo can be caused by an anticollision light, beacon, or flickering cockpit light
  - The physical reactions to the pilot can be nausea, dizziness, grogginess, headaches, confusion, or even unconsciousness
- When there are no lights on the ground, and the stars are bright, pilots have confused the stars for ground lights and inverted the aircraft in an attempt to orient on the "ground lights"
- Night landings, in general, are complicated by the pilot's hampered ability to judge distance

Night Vision

➢ At night, it takes about 30 minutes for the eye to become dark adapted
- These are physical and chemical adjustments of the eye that make vision possible in relative darkness
- The pilot's age and health can increase the time necessary for night adapted sight
- For many pilots, 20 minutes is enough time to become accustomed to the dark
- Avoid looking at any bright light after your eyes are acclimated to the dark

➢ The use of low, white light, cockpit illumination allows the pilot to better read the flight instruments and charts

➢ To maintain dark adaptation, the use of red lighting is the best as it will not affect night vision as much as other colors
- Red printing on the sectional chart will virtually disappear when using red light

➢ Some other ideas to consider when flying at night:
- Avoid smoking, drinking alcohol, or using certain medications that can retard the oxygen level in the blood
  - Eyes need a good supply of oxygen to operate at peak performance
- Maintain a good physical condition
  - Lack of exercise, illness, stress, and fatigue will also adversely affect the oxygen level
- Concentrate on seeing objects
  - If sight becomes blurred, blinking the eyes can help
- Move the eyes more slowly when flying at night than in daylight
- When looking for an object at night, use the off-center scan technique

➢ Altitude is another factor determining how well the pilot can see at night
- The AIM encourages pilots to use supplemental oxygen above 10,000 feet during the day, and above 5,000 feet at night

Night Scanning

- Instrument scanning
  - The pilot should use minimum head movements to do instrument cross-checking
- Scanning the sky for other aircraft is a key factor in collision avoidance
  - The best night viewing technique is to use short, regularly spaced eye movements, concentrating only for a moment on a small area of the total view
    - The FAA suggests that the pilot use peripheral vision at night
    - Scan small sectors of the total view outside the aircraft and use off center viewing
- Eye focus
  - It takes some time, after looking at the flight instruments, to refocus our eyes to the outside
  - The eyes tire more quickly at night because of the constant refocusing between inside and outside viewing

Aircraft Lighting

- Aircraft equipment requirements for VFR flight at night (91.205)
  - Instrumentation
    - See Lesson G10 – *Aircraft Systems, VFR Required Equipment*
  - Electrical energy source
    - An adequate source of electrical energy for all installed electrical and radio equipment
  - Spare fuses
    - One spare set of fuses, or three spare fuses of each kind required, that are accessible to the pilot in flight
  - Lights (discussed below)
- The light requirements include, approved position lights and a red or white anticollision light system
  - Position lights are colored red, green, and white
    - A red light is positioned on the left wing tip
    - A green light is on the right wing tip
    - A white light is on the tail
  - This arrangement allows the pilot, on seeing another aircraft, to determine its direction of flight
- If the aircraft is operated for hire, one electric landing light is needed

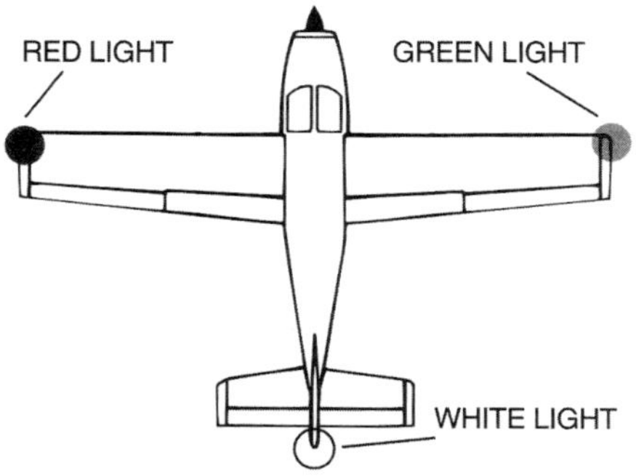

Figure 25-3. – Position lights.

Airport Lighting

- Runways have a variety of lighting systems to assist the pilot at night
- Airport lighting information can be found in:
  - Airport / Facility Directory (A/FD)
  - The sectional chart
  - Notices to Airmen
- Discuss runway light systems, taxiway edge lights, rotating beacons, and pilot controlled lighting with the student, using Chapter 2 of the *AIM* as a reference

➢ Many airport beacons, that seem bright on the ground, are difficult to pick out from the backdrop of city lights
  - Don't become fixated on a beacon from the wrong airport

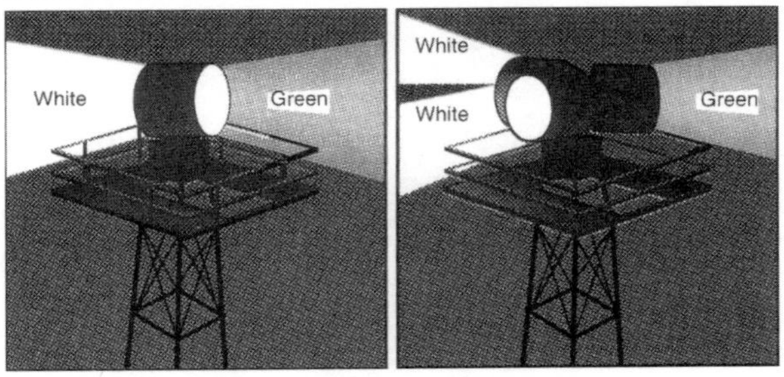

Figure 25-4. – Airport rotating beacons.

Pilot Equipment for Night

➢ Night flying demands better cockpit management
  - Have a flashlight or two with fresh (and spare) batteries within immediate reach
    - A flashlight with D sized batteries is good because the batteries may last longer
    - LEDs last longer and consume less power
    - Better flashlights have two lenses, one clear and one red
  - Organize required charts
  - Become familiar with the cockpit layout, including the location of all controls, instruments, and cockpit lighting
  - Before starting the engine, turn on the anticollision beacon to warn others that the engine is about to start

Chart Use at Night

➢ Acquire all pertinent aeronautical charts
  - Include the proper adjacent charts

➢ Draw course lines in dark ink

➢ Fold each chart in such a way that it can be immediately used without having to search for the necessary information

➢ Be aware that colored lights will not show features on the chart of the same color

Night Flight Preparations

➢ Become familiar with the aeronautical charts necessary for the flight
  - Study the appropriate sectional chart and its symbology, especially regarding cities and towns depicted in yellow, airport rotating beacons, and lighted obstructions

➢ Become familiar with all of the useful night flying information available in the *AIM* and A/FD

➢ Ensure that all flashlights are in good condition

➢ During preflight inspection, ensure that all lighting systems are operating properly

➢ Have a back-up plan

➢ File a flight plan when flying at night

➢ Use radar flight following whenever possible

Night Emergencies

➢ The greatest cause of night flying accidents is flying into adverse weather

➢ Engine failures are no more likely to occur at night than during the day

- Preparation can avert or diminish many emergencies
  - Have a minimal survival kit on board
  - Plan to fly at a higher altitude to increase the aircraft's gliding range
  - Include the engine instruments as part of the scan
  - Pay close attention to the ammeter or load meter
- Discuss the following night emergencies with the student using the AFM/POH and *Airplane Flying Handbook* as references
  - Engine failure or power loss
  - VFR into IMC
  - Electrical problems including full and partial failures
  - In-flight fire

LESSON G26 / G11 – KNOWLEDGE TEST

Private Pilot Knowledge Test

- Ensure that the student is prepared for the knowledge test and passes the exam with an appropriate score
- Review any items missed by the student on the test